De LESSEPS
BUILDER OF SUEZ

MEDITERRANEAN SEA

PORT
SAID

N
W   E
S

SUEZ CANAL

ISMAILIA

LAKE TIMSAH

GREAT BITTER LAKE

LITTLE
BITTER
LAKE

to CAIRO

FRESH
WATER
CANAL
from
CAIRO

SUEZ

GULF
of SUEZ

RED SEA

5
10

20

30

40 ◄ *Scale of miles*

*French Imperial yacht,
"Aigle" brought Empress
Eugenie to Suez 1869* ►

◄ *Suez Canal 1869*

De LESSEPS
BUILDER OF SUEZ

by
LAURA LONG

Decorations by
CLOTILDE EMBREE FUNK

LONGMANS, GREEN and CO.
NEW YORK • **LONDON** • **TORONTO**

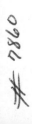

LONGMANS, GREEN AND CO., INC.
55 FIFTH AVENUE, NEW YORK 3

LONGMANS, GREEN AND CO., LTD.
6 & 7 CLIFFORD STREET, LONDON W 1

LONGMANS, GREEN AND CO.
20 CRANFIELD ROAD, TORONTO 16

DE LESSEPS: BUILDERS OF SUEZ

PUBLISHED SIMULTANEOUSLY IN THE DOMINION OF CANADA BY
LONGMANS, GREEN AND CO., TORONTO

FIRST EDITION

LIBRARY OF CONGRESS CATALOG CARD NUMBER 58-7328

Printed in the United States of America

CHAPTER ONE

A PRETTY French housemaid came running, her heels clicking against the stones in the garden path, her face bright with excitement.

"Un p'tit fils, M'sieur!" she called to the man who was walking aimlessly through the frost-deadened garden. "C'est arrivé."

The French consul smiled happily. "Never too many sons for France, child!" he replied, as he ran toward the house and up the steep stairs to his wife's bedroom.

He was glad this new son had seized the good fortune of being born under the brilliant star of Napoleon. Mathieu de Lesseps was a friend of Napoleon's. He had pledged his life to his service, in the French Foreign Office. During his last tour of duty in Egypt, from which he had returned barely in time for his son to be born on French soil, he had made a recommendation to Napoleon that would become the long arm of destiny to this newly born child. Mathieu de Lesseps himself would never know this, but the child would. And his whole life would be changed by this one fact.

When the French fleet was defeated by Lord Nelson's British navy, it became necessary for the French to withdraw from Egypt, which country they had controlled. Napoleon asked his French consul to suggest a man to head the new autonomous government in Egypt, a man friendly to France. And De Lesseps had suggested Mehemet Ali Bey, a Turkish general who preferred the French to the conquering British and would keep alive French interests in Egypt.

The consul was proud of this deed he had done for Napoleon. Someday he would tell his new son all about it—this son who was being born here in Versailles, on this nineteenth day of November, 1805.

In the darkened bedroom, earsplitting cries vibrated from the knit blanket the midwife was holding. The woman was laughing, and jouncing the blanket up and down, to quiet the baby.

When at last she could be heard, she remarked, "Small enough, I'd say. He's a short little fellow. But what a lusty noise he makes upon his arrival! As if he'd made up his mind already he's going to be heard from!"

The child's mother smiled fondly at her husband and pulled at a lock of dark hair that hung over her white forehead.

"I've given him a name, Mathieu. I call him Fernando."

The name surprised him. The name of a Spanish prince, for the son of a French consul? But his beautiful dark-haired wife was Spanish, of the great Spanish family, Montijo. He would not quarrel with the name. He would merely translate it to French.

"He is a Frenchman, chérie. We will call him Ferdinand." He stooped, to kiss his wife's forehead gently, and as he did so, he remembered something that pleased him. "There was another Ferdinand. Remember? Duke Ferdinand of Austria united Austria and Hungary. And now that Napoleon's Austrian campaign is succeeding, it is a good name, ma chérie."

"May the terrible wars all be ended, and may the world know only peace through his lifetime! That is what I most wish for him," she said.

The new Frenchman was screaming in protest at his first bath. His mother smiled.

"It is good he has spirit," she said. "He will need it. He has three older brothers."

The midwife brought the child to his mother, and quickly matters of state were forgotten in the important business of examining the new baby's head and hands and feet.

But affairs of state would always play a part in the lives of this French family. Before Ferdinand was two years old, his father was sent to the seacoast town of Leghorn in northern Italy on the Ligurian sea, from which vantage point he was to keep an eye on the shipping activities of the new Triple Alliance that was pledged to stop the advances of Napoleon's armies.

Not that politics made the slightest difference to the De Lesseps children, except to decide where they would be living. In Leghorn, which they learned to call by its soft Italian name of Livorno, they watched the sea and the ships and enjoyed the warm Italian sun and the soft winds from the Mediterranean.

The old, inconvenient house in which they lived was grandly called "castle," since an Italian prince had once lived there. It had an arched gate that opened on the street, though the gate was kept locked when the children were playing in its shadow.

But Ferdinand was forever to remember those autumn days when the winter wood was brought for the numerous castle fireplaces. The woodcutter's arrival was foretold by the shouting children who suddenly appeared out of nowhere and began running after his camels.

The porter would throw open the gate, its hinges creaking from age and salt air, and the children would see a sight they had never beheld before.

A half dozen camels stood, with brown necks outstretched, eyes blinking sleepily, great logs of wood piled on their backs in stout baskets. They seemed to be patiently waiting for the gates to admit them, yet once the way was clear, they appeared not to see it, or else were fully convinced that they would not enter. The drivers pulled on their reins, and beat them with sticks, the children yelled at them and slapped them on the back, but the camels merely arched their necks longer than ever and walked proudly past the open gate, as though they could not see it. The children would stop them from going far, and the drivers would turn them back toward the gate again, and again they would seem not to see it. Time after time this would happen until finally, and for no particular reason that anyone could see, unless the haughty camels had grown tired of their load and of the whole foolish business, they would turn calmly through the gate and stand blinking their weak eyes while the wood was unloaded.

To a three-year-old child such as Ferdinand de Lesseps, the camels must have looked like primeval giants. Most children would have been afraid. But Ferdinand knew no fear, to his nurse's dismay, and he ran to the camels and pretended to help unload the heavy sticks of wood. He learned the feel of the camel's rough tongue and soft nose. He was completely delighted with the whole dramatic performance and ran, singing loudly, in and out of the camels' long legs, with everyone rushing at him to keep him from being stepped on.

This was what he would later remember of those two years at Livorno, and he might not have remembered even this, if half a century later other camels, which he was to know much more intimately, had not recalled these first ones to his mind.

The next tour of duty for Ferdinand's father was on

Corfu, one of the Ionian Islands. He was to be governor of all the Ionian Islands, and it was a position of great responsibility at that time. France had won Austria and Hungary at Austerlitz, but the British had defeated the French navy at Trafalgar. This defeat had caused Napoleon to issue the Berlin Decree, which warned all subjects of France—including those newly won subjects of conquered nations—that any trade with Great Britain would be considered an act of treason. If France could not defeat England's navy in battle, then she could close the seaways to British shipping.

Not that Great Britain would meekly submit to the Berlin Decree. There were rumors that British troops were on their way to Spain, where Napoleon had placed his brother Joseph on the throne of the deposed Spanish ruler, Ferdinand's namesake. Corfu would be a dangerous mission, and Mathieu could not risk exposing his family to its dangers.

"Pisa will be safer than Leghorn. And you have friends there," he said to his wife. "I shall move you to Pisa, and there you will wait for me."

CHAPTER TWO

PISA WAS crowded with French army and navy and foreign service families. Most of them had fathers and sons and husbands away at war. But they shared one another's troubles and heartaches and found amusement among themselves that made the waiting bearable. Catherine de Lesseps' heart was heavy with the knowledge that Corfu might be under British fire at any moment. But the thought that among her friends were many with greater fears than hers made her assume a cheerfulness she did not always feel.

It was not an easy situation for a young wife with four lively little boys. The youngest one especially seemed always to be in trouble of some sort, and always so full of charm that he could smile his way out of any situation, no matter how unhappy it might be. Perhaps, to keep Ferdinand good and obedient, she drew for him a more heroic picture of his father than she realized. Certainly it was soon plain that in Ferdinand's eyes his own father was a far greater figure than the emperor everyone thought was so wonderful.

With the double responsibility on her shoulders, she tried to teach her children everything she could. Pisa had once been the home of the great Galileo, who had discovered the law of gravity. With difficulty Catherine persuaded her children to go with her to see the university where Galileo had taught and where he had carried on so many of his experiments, and from which he had been driven because he insisted that the world moved round the sun. The children would have preferred one more excursion to the Arno River, which had such a fascination for Ferdinand that it almost frightened his mother. Why would a boy be so bemused by a river? He could ask a thousand questions about the Arno. And she could answer not more than a dozen of them. So the visit to the university would serve several purposes, not the least of them being to coax her youngest son away from the river.

She drove the lesson home as firmly as she knew how. Here was this man Galileo who had discovered a truth that others doubted. But he did not let their doubts change him. When one is sure he knows, nothing that anyone else may say or do should make any difference. It didn't to Galileo. Even persecution did not make him deny his truth. It took courage and self-confidence, and he had both. A man can accomplish almost anything, if he has courage and faith in himself.

"And he finally proved he was right, of course. Truth will prevail, always. Not even when his persecutors made him sign a retraction of his statement that the earth moved did he give up his truth. Even then he said, 'But the world does move, you know.' Never let anyone turn you away from what you know to be true," Catherine concluded.

Before many days had passed, Ferdinand was showing his mother that the story of Galileo had been heard and digested. One morning as he was dressing, he stood looking out of the window, daydreaming. Somehow the thought of Galileo came to mind, and he stood there wondering how anyone knew that Galileo was right, and how he had been proved so. One way, of course, was to test Galileo's rule of falling bodies. Just because something happened to an apple, why must it necessarily happen also to a human being? It seemed to him possible that the great Galileo could be mistaken. The next step, then, was to throw open the window and test Galileo's law of motion for himself. With arms spread like wings, Ferdinand leaned forward and let his body fall from the upstairs window. Hardly did he have time to note that a falling body really did gather momentum as it fell, when his body struck the ground with a dull thud and he was conscious of intense pain in the arm that had somehow folded under him.

He cried out, and both mother and nurse came running. In a little while, the doctor had been called and Ferdinand's broken arm was firmly tied to a stick and he was warned against moving it for some time. But he had proved for himself that Galileo was right and this eased his discontent in having to be confined to the house.

His greatest disappointment was that the useless arm made him miss his riding lessons, which of all the many activities he had tried, he liked best. His riding master was a young military officer, Captain Courrier.

Captain Courrier was not only a good teacher but also a good friend who knew that a child must be treated with respect and affection. The captain had seldom had a pupil show such aptitude for horsemanship as this eight-year-old son of the lovely Madame de Lesseps. The boy learned so easily and so well that it was not long before Captain Courrier was looking forward to the daily lesson as eagerly as Ferdinand.

On his Arabian horse—the horse that belonged to his absent father, with Captain Courrier beside him, Ferdinand could go far beyond that tight little world of his that was prescribed by his nurse's and his mother's guardianship. The world and the horse were his, for him to control and persuade. Captain Courrier would go anywhere Ferdinand wished to go, so long as the leaning tower that rose above Pisa remained in sight. And always it appeared to Ferdinand that the tower seemed to be leaning toward him.

One day, as they were coming home from an early morning canter, they first heard and then saw a French messenger running through the streets, proclaiming news of some sort. The captain called to Ferdinand that they would follow him, to learn the news. And then, before the child could make anything out of the messenger's words, Captain Courrier drew his reins tight and turned his horse around.

"Come," he said to his pupil. "Gallop your horse. We must tell our news to your mother. It could mean your father will soon be home again."

Ferdinand did as the captain told him. He even touched his horse's flank lightly with one spur. The horse's feet struck sparks from the stones of the street, and the boy could feel the wind on his face as the horse ran faster and faster. But he did not once lose control of the animal. He held fast to the reins, and felt delight in the speed at which he was riding. Never before had he been permitted to ride so fast.

The only words he could make out when he listened to the messenger were, "Vive le roi! Vive le roi!" But he had supposed of course that the fellow was cheering for Napoleon. Now at home once more, he was learning his mistake.

"The western allies have seized Paris," he heard Captain Courrier tell his mother. "Napoleon has been exiled and Louis Bourbon has taken the throne. Madame, this is some of Talleyrand's doings."

"Oh no! No!" cried Madame de Lesseps, and she looked frightened. For some reason Ferdinand felt he should stand close beside her and hold her hand tightly.

"And Mathieu? Does this mean he will be a prisoner of war? What will they do to him, those western allies who hate France?"

"They may let him come home to you, madame," answered the captain. "There is no longer need for him to play watchdog to the allies' shipping."

This seemed to surprise her. Ferdinand was watching her face closely. He saw the color come to her cheeks as she stood, silent and thoughtful, her hand lightly touching her dark hair.

"There is sometimes good in evil things, n'est-ce pas, mon capitaine?" shesaid softly, putting her hand on Ferdinand's head and drawing him closer beside her. "But—but Napoleon—in exile! It will take me a while to believe that."

"Yet it seems to be true, madame. You could, if you liked, go see for yourself. He is only as far off as Elba. Less than a hundred miles from Pisa."

"No, Captain Courrier, I do not care to see the emperor. But you—you will go?"

"Oui, madame. There might still be some service he will be needing that I could do for him. You are right, it does take a while to believe this."

The captain left them then, and never again did Ferdinand ride by his side over the cobbled streets of Pisa.

Anxious days followed. No one could say what would happen to the husbands and sons and fathers of those French women and children who were waiting for their return in Pisa. Many among those French expatriates quickly changed politics. They were no longer Napoleonists. They were Royalists.

"Vive le roi! Vive le roi!" they cried.

The change brought an end to many a friendship. Would the Royalists look for reasons to inform on the Napoleonists, as proof of their royal loyalty?

When word finally came from her husband, Catherine de Lesseps told no one outside the immediate household, and even those were warned to say nothing to anyone. Mathieu, the faithful agent of Napoleon's government, had finally been forced to surrender to the British, almost at the same hour in which the new King of France had been proclaimed. He had turned over the control of all those strategic islands that looked toward Asia and Africa and it had made him feel a traitor, even though it had been done at the insistence of his own government. There had been nothing else to do but surrender, if he obeyed orders. He was returning to Paris and would meet his family there. Catherine was to take the children and the household and leave immediately. She and her husband would probably arrive about the same time.

The reunion was not a happy one. The new government had commanded that Mathieu surrender, even though he had at first sent back his refusal to do so. He had explained his reasons quite plainly. If he surrendered the Ionian Islands to the British, it would mean that France would lose any chance she might have in the future to enter Asia or Africa. It was far too great a price to pay for British friendship.

But the Bourbon king would need Great Britain if he wished to keep his throne. So the order was sent to Corfu: "Surrender Corfu and return to Paris immediately."

Upon his arrival home, Mathieu de Lesseps found the Foreign Office upset over his first refusal to obey their orders. He tried to explain that he still believed it his duty to do what was best for France, rather than blindly obey the orders of some distant official. He learned for the first time that his fellow attaché, who had been left at Corfu, had already been imprisoned for treason. The king was taking no chances. As for Mathieu himself, he was lucky. He would merely be demoted to vice consul, rather than consul. The news hurt. A foreign diplomat's salary at best was barely sufficient for living. A vice consul's was hardly enough for a single man. And Mathieu had an ever-increasing family. In fact, Napoleon himself had once asked him, "How do you ever keep count of your children, Count de Lesseps? You have so many of them." Yet the one thing any man in foreign service must learn above all others is to accept his government's decisions—especially when he could do nothing to change them. In the strict sense of the word, he had indeed been guilty of insubordination— but it was only because his deep love for France had made it impossible for him to act in a way that he felt would harm her.

And then, with even greater suddenness than the first message had come to Pisa, the news arrived in Paris that Napoleon had come back from Elba and had deposed the king! The volatile French went mad with the dramatic announcement. And suddenly everybody in Paris was again Napoleonist.

The whole picture was changed. Instead of being an outcast in his own department, Ferdinand's father became a hero. Napoleon ordered that he be rewarded for his bold stand at Corfu. He was made a Count of the Empire and given a prefecture, a city over which he might rule for so long as the rulers of France approved, he and his sons and his grandsons after him.

There was one more favor the new count wished to ask of his emperor. He had watched his children, and there was one whom he felt might follow in his father's footsteps as a representative of his country.

"My son Ferdinand, sire, child though he be, wishes to serve France in her Foreign Office. Have not De Lesseps always served France in this way? But he must know many things to be a good servant of France. And so, more than the prefecture, for which I assure you I

am most grateful, I would like my son Ferdinand to
have a far better education than I, at my salary, could
afford to give him. Would you see that he has such a
chance, sire?"

Of all the honors Mathieu de Lesseps received at that
time, the one he most highly prized was the grant the
French government made him for the education of his
son Ferdinand.

Later, when Napoleon was again exiled, this time forever, this was the only honor not taken away from him.
What a good investment for France that grant was to
prove to be!

CHAPTER THREE

WITH LOUIS XVIII on the French throne, and Napoleon in exile, the good fortune of Mathieu de Lesseps ended. He was deprived of his prefecture and his title, and, what was worse, was never again to serve his government in France. He would have only small Mediterranean posts the rest of his life and would never be promoted.

His father's misfortunes made little impression on young Ferdinand, who was enrolled at the Lycée Napoleon when he was ten years old. Hardly had the classes for the new term been formed than the name of the school was changed from the Lycée Napoleon to the College of Henri IV, so determined was the new régime to wipe the name of Napoleon from young French minds.

Ferdinand was soon to find that he was rather better than average in his studies, and that he could outclass most of his schoolmates on the playground. He learned the usual Latin and Greek, and once again met his old friend, Galileo, and recalled the visit his mother had made him take to the Pisa university. But it was in sports that he really excelled. His small stature and amazing energy gave him advantage over other boys. He was lithe and quick at fencing and boxing, and once, to his great delight, won the decision of the judges in a boxing match with one of the sons of Louis Philippe of the royal house of Orleans, who had not yet taken his place on the throne of France.

He did not outgrow the fascination that rivers always brought to him. At Pisa it had been the Arno. In Paris it was the Seine. Rivers were full of mystery for him, moving forever to some destination that he could never discover. Towns along rivers seemed to be joined together in some sort of secret bond by the rivers that cut their way through them. Ferdinand was a strong swimmer, for to him a river was always friendly.

Once while he was at the Lycée, he and a group of boys had been picnicking at St. Germain, and toward evening they waited at the river for the ferry that would take them back to school. The ferry was late and the boys grew more and more impatient.

"We could swim across the river here and still beat the ferry," one of them said, laughing.

But Ferdinand turned the joke into a challenge. "Why don't we?" he suggested. "We shall swim and see who gets there first."

The suggestion set them all chattering. Some thought the idea all nonsense. Some agreed to try it. And some brought up objections that would have to be met before deciding to swim so wide a river.

"The Seine is wider than it looks here," they said. "And what will we do with our clothes?"

Ferdinand quickly proceeded to show them. He took off his shoes and tied them together with his garters. He put his shirt and his cotton stockings inside his wool hat and put the hat on his head. Then he found a long stick, and holding it upright, he hung his coat, vest and breeches over the top of it. Stripped to his underwear, he waded into the river, and holding the stick aloft in one hand began to swim with the other.

He soon found difficulties he had not considered. The river held hidden currents that threatened to draw him under. It took all the strength of two strong young arms to battle those currents. No hand was left free now to hold his clothes aloft. Time and again, he would drop the stick and give all his strength to the current, and then he would reach back and recover his clothes and once again hold the stick aloft, where the going was easier. It took twice the strength he had thought it would take, between battling the current and saving his wearing apparel. And the river seemed to grow wider, the farther he swam. His arms ached and he couldn't help swallowing water, and he knew that his breath was getting shorter and shorter. But he didn't give up. He couldn't. Once he had started, there was nothing to do but go on to the finish.

He tried lying on his back, until he could breathe

easier. He tried treading water. Every breath was a pain now. And then, just as he had despaired of ever making the other shore, his big toe touched mud. If he had had enough breath left, he would have shouted. All he could do was grin, get on his feet and walk to shore. He had beaten the ferry!

Foolhardy and unnecessary though it was, this adventure made him a hero among his schoolmates. This he enjoyed, and did what he could to hold the position during his stay at the Lycée.

The defeat of Napoleon and the resulting turmoil in political circles made young Frenchmen conscious of political questions at a much earlier age than they would have been in more normal times. And the professors at the Lycée did what they could to channel their interest into sound political thinking. It might, indeed, be these very boys, these young aristocrats, who would one day lead France into more stable political waters. It was important to France that they be carefully taught.

So Ferdinand was exposed to numerous schools of political and philosophical thought. But the political philosopher who appealed to him most was Claude Henri, Comte de St. Simon, who dreamed of a world without wars, in which wars would be undesirable because they would interfere with a free flow of trade that would be far more profitable to the nations of the world than wars.

This free trade was to be made possible by two great

ocean highways that would shorten the world's trade routes. One of these would join the Red Sea and the Mediterranean, possibly in Egypt, and the other would join the Pacific and Atlantic oceans in America. Ferdinand promptly adopted St. Simon's dream as his own, and held it deep in his heart for years, until certain things happened that made the dream seem on the way to realization.

There was another of St. Simon's precepts that Ferdinand always remembered. The goal of all government, said St. Simon, should be to give "each man a vocation according to his capacity, and to each capacity a recompense according to its worth." And he thought of his father, whose recompense since the banishment of Napoleon had been far, far less than his true capacity.

It was a day when the world had seen too much war, and when peace seemed to be the most desirable and most prized object of government everywhere. Such times in history made idealists of the world's youth. Ferdinand de Lesseps was no exception. But he was also made a realist by the stern necessities of life.

Most of his friends at school had much more money to spend than his father could afford to send him. Yet it seemed to him important that he live up to the standards set by these sons of French aristocrats. Therefore, during the last two years of his stay at the Lycée, he held a part-time job at the Paris post office. This gave him the

extra spending money he needed. And upon his graduation, while he waited to be assigned to some station in
Foreign Service, he began a correspondence with his
favorite uncle, Barthélemy de Lesseps.

This uncle was the adventurer of the family. Ferdinand had read and re-read a book he had found in the
library at home, a book in which his uncle described his
own adventures in his early years in the French Foreign
Service. That had been forty years ago, but to Ferdinand
the story, no matter how often he read it, seemed to be
happening in the present.

Because of his gift for languages, which all the De
Lesseps seemed to have, Barthélemy had been chosen to
accompany an expedition of general discovery under
Jean de Galaup, Comte de Laperouse. It was during the
reign of Louis XVI and the expedition consisted of two
well-equipped vessels, manned by French scientists.
Barthélemy was included because he could speak and
understand the Russian language.

The expedition rounded Cape Horn and explored the
western coast of the United States, since France was interested in the new continent in which she held territory
and was even then establishing more forts in the interior
of the country, to increase her trade in furs.

They went as far north as Canada, and then across
the Pacific, still heading north, to Kamchatka. By that
time both money and supplies were giving out. The only

way they could possibly continue the expedition was to send someone back to France, overland, with the scientific records of the expedition so far, to convince the French court that the expedition should be continued. And for this dangerous journey, Barthélemy de Lesseps was selected.

He crossed Siberia by snowshoes and dog sled, every wintry mile a challenge to human endurance and fortitude. Time after time he barely escaped death, first from freezing, and then from starvation. By the time he arrived at Versailles, he was a broken wreck of a man, but the Laperouse records were still intact. And for some time Barthélemy was honored at the French court. Dressed as a Kamchatka hunter, he told his story over and over again among court circles. He was the season's sensation.

The money was, as a consequence, soon raised, and a supply ship was sent to the relief of the expedition, with Barthélemy de Lesseps on board to direct the captain. But when they came to the place where Barthélemy was certain he had left his companions, there were no longer any ships there. Nor could they find any trace of them, or anyone who had seen them. Someone did recall seeing such ships at Botany Bay, but when the rescue party went there, they found nothing. They had vanished as though they had been swept off the sea. It was as though the expedition had never existed.

Barthélemy, who had been stationed in Russia at the time the expedition had started, returned there, hoping to hear news of them sometime. And then had come the French Revolution, and he had been ordered back to France.

The eagerness with which Ferdinand had always listened to his uncle's adventures had made him a favorite of the old man's. Barthélemy was, at the time of his nephew's graduation, stationed at Lisbon, Portugal, and he asked that his nephew be sent to him as his assistant. It would be Ferdinand's first charge. He would have much to learn, and his uncle would prove a good instructor.

Ferdinand stayed in Lisbon under his uncle's tutelage for three years, and then joined his father, who was stationed at Tunis. But when he went to Tunis he took along with him the vivid memory of Uncle Barthélemy's often-repeated axiom: "Always remember, the world is your home, but France is your love."

And he thanked God that he had been born in a family of diplomats who could give him such excellent training in his first stations. Both father and uncle had been trained under Talleyrand, once Napoleon's foreign minister, but now guiding the destinies of the House of Bourbon. And both father and uncle had repeated to him the little speech Talleyrand had always made to his new consuls, before giving them their instructions.

"How many things a man must know to make a good consul—for his duties are endless in their variety and quite of a different character from those of other officials of the Foreign Office; they demand a mass of practical knowledge for which special education is required. Consuls should be able to fulfill, in the event of necessity, the duties of judge, arbitrator and reconciler. They must be able to do the work of a notary, sometimes that of a commissioner in the navy. They have to look after sanitary matters, and from them is expected, owing to their general relations, a clear idea of the state of transportation and navigation and of industry peculiar to their places of residence."

He did not add that a consul was also expected to make a pleasing impression in society, that he must be a good dancer, a skillful conversationalist, capable of drawing out the views of others; he must be a success with the ladies, without arousing jealousy in their escorts; in short, he must be always charming, always agreeable, yet ever alert to the first faint signs of danger.

Yes, the new vice consul to Tunis seemed to be well qualified for his new position.

CHAPTER FOUR

ONCE AGAIN the French government changed heads, when in 1830 Charles X, younger brother of Louis XVIII, was deposed and Louis Philippe, of the House of Orleans, was given the crown. News came slowly to Tunis, but when it came, it was good news to the De Lesseps.

Louis Philippe had spent his youth in exile, first in America and then in England. His foreign education had given him ideas of democracy, and the change, it seemed, should be good for France. The change should also be particularly good for Mathieu de Lesseps, whose long exile might well be ended now, with Louis Philippe home in France again. Who would know better than the new emperor the ignominy of exile? Who would better understand the longing a Frenchman has to return to France? And the additional fact that Ferdinand and the king's sons had been schoolmates made it possible to approach the new ruler. Mathieu wrote to the Foreign Office, but he wrote also to the king himself. He was a sick old man now, full of bitterness and disappointment. Surely France would grant him this last favor before he died.

Such requests took time. And even when the favor had been granted, transportation was slow and the news was old before it reached those concerned with it. Mathieu de Lesseps, unable to bear the long waiting, was dead when the packet finally arrived at Tunis granting him leave to return to France.

Ferdinand arrived in France with his father's dead body in the year 1832. He had been ordered home for re-assignment, and his mother, fulfilling her husband's last dream, decided to make her home in France now, just as they had planned to do. The loss of his father was very real to Ferdinand. No longer would he have the advantage of his father's experience and knowledge. He would have to trust his own judgment, make his own decisions, recognizing his own unhappy inclination to act upon impulse, without weighing consequences. Would he still be able to feel his father's steadying hand on his shoulder?

He was assigned to Egypt. That same Mehemet Ali whom Mathieu de Lesseps had picked from the Turkish army to be viceroy of Egypt at the time of Napoleon's Egyptian campaign was Egypt's pasha. Strange that he should be sent to his father's old post at such a time. Would Mehemet Ali remember?

The first few scattered cases of a cholera epidemic were beginning to startle the coast towns of France at the time the vice consul's ship was to sail for Egypt. Rumors were whispered in Marseilles, and the ship's passengers were uneasy, but they breathed a deep sigh of relief as the ship dipped her sails and slipped into the sea, headed for Alexandria. Had they waited a few more days, they would have been quarantined in the harbor for a month, at least.

The voyage proved uneventful until the day before they were to dock at Alexandria. That evening a sailor complained of a headache, and before morning he was dead. The news shocked everyone on board. The captain promptly buried the body at sea, but the port authorities at Alexandria had to be notified.

The port authorities ordered the ship to sit in mid-ocean for two weeks. Then, if no more cholera had appeared, they could put into port.

Two weeks of inaction at the very end of a voyage was nobody's idea of entertainment. The passengers spent their time grumbling at the delay, blaming the captain for starting, the sailor for dying, and finally agreeing that they were probably lucky that it was no worse than it was.

The French consul to Alexandria improved his professional education by reading the captain's books on sanitation in times of epidemics of cholera. In Alexandria, the French minister to Egypt sympathized with his vice consul and did what he could to relieve the young man's tedium. He sent a messenger to the quarantined ship with a bundle of books. This new young diplomat might well employ his time to advantage during his quarantine, reading about the country he was about to serve.

The twenty-seven-year-old career diplomat opened the books eagerly. He turned the pages of first one and then another and finally fell upon one of the volumes with an avidity that would have amazed the foreign minister. The book was the published report of the findings of Napoleon's engineer, Lapere, and it concerned the surveys and plans for a proposed canal that would join the Red Sea and the Mediterranean. Here was the very thing that had most interested Ferdinand at the university—St. Simon's project for world peace, a trade route to be used in peace by all the world's nations! Why, Napoleon had actually considered building one of those very canals!

There was much in the Lapere book that Ferdinand already knew. He knew there had been a canal joining the Nile and the Red Sea three thousand years before, that it had finally silted over and become useless until, in the time of Darius, it was rebuilt to provide a passage from Asia to Europe during the Persian wars. His father had told him enough of Napoleon's campaign in Egypt for him to know that Napoleon had ordered that Egypt was to be taken, the English driven out, and their trade routes demolished. It was with the idea of giving France a new route to India that would shut England out, that Napoleon had ordered Lapere to survey the possibility of building a canal that would join the Nile to the Mediterranean Sea. This was the report he was reading now, and he found it enthralling.

Lapere believed that a canal could be built at a cost of twenty-five or thirty million francs, that it would have to be a locks canal because of the difference in level of the Red Sea and the Mediterranean. He did not believe that a harbor could be built at Pelusium. It would have to be a round-about canal, going from Alexandria to Suez by way of Bulaq, Serapeum and Shaluf. He believed the canal could furnish as continuous a trade route as the Cape of Good Hope and that it could be more easily made exclusive to whatever country controlled it. Which, of course, Lapere knew would be France.

But Ferdinand de Lesseps, reading Lapere's words, knew that such a canal, if it were to bring peace to the world, must be controlled not by France or by any other one nation, but by the united nations of the world. Egypt was the gateway through which all trade must pass. She would never be free of foreign influence. Therefore her friendship was of the utmost importance to every nation in the world. The thought made his new position seem of even greater importance than Ferdinand had first realized. The good will of Egypt might well mean world trade, and particularly Indian trade, with France. Could Mehemet Ali be persuaded to build such a canal as Lapere had dreamed of? He was a man who, though not a smart one, was making his country strong through the building of great public works. A Suez canal might be the crown of his reign. The thought made the days of idle waiting seem almost exciting to the new vice consul.

Immediately after the quarantine was lifted, Ferdinand hurried to the Foreign Office to report for duty.

"The books were lifesavers," he told the foreign minister. "I can never thank you. The best one of them all was the Lapere report."

"We thought it might be valuable to you to know our country's background in Egyptian affairs."

"That canal could be a great instrument of peace," suggested Ferdinand.

"Or of war." The minister smiled.

"Why doesn't the pasha build it?" he asked.

"Perhaps for the same classic reason that others have refused to build it—he does not care to furnish a trade route for infidels."

"Meaning—us?"

"Meaning all Christian nations, for all I know. But if you are so interested, why not ask the pasha himself? See that you use diplomacy, though. I shall make an appointment for you to see Mehemet Ali tomorrow."

"My father recommended him to Napoleon. What sort of man is this Mehemet Ali?"

"A big brute in appearance, without education, but with a great deal of innate shrewdness. You will see what he is like when you talk with him."

CHAPTER FIVE

THE VICEROY greeted the French vice consul effusively. "Your father was my friend. The son of my friend is doubly welcome to Egypt. Had it not been for your father—and the great Napoleon, to be sure—I might still have been a Turkish soldier instead of the ruler of Egypt."

"From what I hear, sir, my father was a good judge of men. What you are doing in Egypt proves that his recommendation was good," replied Ferdinand politely.

"We have learned much from the west," Mehemet Ali went on. "In time we may have learned enough that we can be free of all western influence. But now—we have western engineers for our public works, western teachers for our schools, western doctors and scientists, helping us solve Egypt's problems."

Yet there was a problem even the imported teachers had not been able to solve. Mehemet Ali's youngest son, Said, was a very fat and surly child of ten and the mere sight of the boy, or the mention of his name, seemed to irritate his father. Hardly had Mehemet Ali met the French vice consul than he looked at him speculatively.

"Word has come to me that you are a good horseman," said the viceroy. "We shall see that you have a fine horse while you are with us here." Suddenly he clapped his hands loudly and a servant appeared from the shadows.

"Bring my son Said to me," he ordered.

The boy came, pudgy and awkward and sadly self-conscious, embarrassed at having to meet a stranger.

"My son Said," said the father. "Look at him. Look at all that fat." And he pounded his beefy fist against the boy's stomach.

The child flushed and drew back, biting his lip as though holding back words he dared not say.

Mehemet Ali turned to De Lesseps. "You ride horseback. Do you think this boy could lose some of that fat riding horseback?"

"He might lose some," admitted Ferdinand, trying to smile at the boy whose eyes were dark with resentment. He was thinking how much the boy resembled the father.

"Could you teach him to ride well? And to lose weight while he is doing it?"

"I could try, sir," answered Ferdinand.

"Would you like that, Said? Would you like to ride a horse as well as our Arabian generals?"

The child hung his head, saying nothing. Ferdinand grinned at him.

"You seem eager. Not afraid of a horse, are you, son?"

"No, sir. But I can't seem to stay on a horse's back."

"You will," promised De Lesseps.

The boy's father clapped for a servant. "Bring me Said's report card. I want the vice consul to see it."

"Now see," he said, showing the card to his caller. "All these studies—fourteen different subjects he studies— what for, I don't know—or care, really. It's these western teachers. He must know to read. He must know to spell. He must know this. He must know that. I didn't learn to read until I was forty years old. Can't read very well, even now. But does it matter? I pay no attention to all these columns. What he does in these studies is all right —whatever it is. But this—here in this column—this is what I watch close. His weight. If he loses a pound one week, I reward him. If he gains a pound, then I punish him. But soon I will run out of punishments. Two pounds and a quarter he has gained since last week. So I must punish."

"Why?" asked De Lesseps.

"Why?" The viceroy blinked at his visitor, looking puzzled.

"Yes, why? If it doesn't do any good?"

Mehemet Ali's great bulk shook with silent laughter. "A fair enough question, Consul de Lesseps. But how else can I teach him that he must not look like a hog?"

The vice consul picked up the report card. He counted the fourteen subjects and saw that the child had done well with most of them. Fourteen of them! No wonder the boy was unhappy and sullen. How could there be any time left for playing?

He looked at Said, and smiled. "With a schedule like this, Said, I am amazed that you haven't faded completely away. It is an achievement to be able to gain weight in spite of such hard work."

The boy looked surprised. At first he seemed confused. He was not used to praise. Could the vice consul be teasing him, the way everyone always teased him? But the vice consul seemed serious. There was approval in his eyes. The child's face lighted. But he said nothing. He spoke but seldom when his father was present. He knew with bitterness that nothing he ever said seemed to please his father.

"Hold up that punishment this week, sire," the vice consul suggested. "Let me have the boy for an hour or so every day. Perhaps by next week you will be buying a present."

Ferdinand was remembering his own childhood in Italy, and the pleasure he had known riding with Captain Courrier. Maybe the riding lessons would ease the pressure from the fourteen different subjects. Anyway, it seemed to De Lesseps that what the boy needed was not reward or punishment, but a friend, a friend in whom he could confide, in whose presence he could feel secure and could know he was not being laughed at.

Soon the young prince came to look upon the vice consul's quarters as a haven of rest, a sanctuary from royal teachers. The riding lessons quickly lost their terror, and he was able to enjoy them. One could also escape from studies by riding away from them. At first he had fallen off his horse more than he had stayed on, a circumstance that did manage to jar loose a few pounds of unsightly fat. But when the lesson was over, the boy would go to De Lesseps' quarters where he was made to feel free to stare idly into space if he wished to do so, or to sleep, or to read, or to talk about the things in which he was most interested. And these things seemed to be myriad. He was an intelligent child, curious about the world about him. And when they found that they had one great interest in common, their friendship was sealed forever, for both were eagerly curious about the old Egyptian canal. Often their rides were along the old earthworks of the ancient canal, tracing its course.

As the riding improved and their friendship ripened, the weeks for reward outnumbered the weeks when Said expected punishment. No longer did he need to comfort his aching spirit with the pleasure of food. Not, of course, that he did not still enjoy a hearty meal, plus an occasional sweet between meals. But food was no longer his greatest interest.

"Said, you have lost weight again this week," Ferdinand would rejoice with him. "According to your father, that means a reward. What do you want the most at this minute?"

"Macaroni." The hungry prince grinned.

The vice consul grinned back at him. "When I was

your age, I was living in Italy. I, too, learned to like macaroni. Come home with me, and we shall have it for supper."

Over steaming dishes of macaroni, with butter and cheese melting on top of it, they cemented a friendship that was to last forever. And Said lost his surliness and absorbed some of his teacher's gay good humor and learned to talk easily and well.

De Lesseps had been in Egypt two years when a serious epidemic of Asiatic cholera broke out in both Alexandria and Cairo, the two capitals. Luckily, part of Mehemet Ali's public works had consisted of a rude road joining the two cities, so that it was possible to get from one to the other in a short time. The French vice consul began working immediately to set up hospitals and to obtain drugs and clean clothing for the victims and their families. He even turned the consulate itself into a hospital and made constant trips back and forth from Alexandria to Cairo. He used his unusual powers of persuasion on the most terror-stricken to convince them that it would be better for their loved ones to be in a lazaretto, where they could be properly treated and given proper medicines, than for them to stay at home and expose others of the family to the scourge. When overworked doctors gave up, saying they could do no more, Ferdinand would take over, sitting at bedsides, comforting, encouraging, giving hope to the hopeless. Once in Cairo he found forty-two men in one room in an overcrowded lazaretto, where even the doctors refused to enter. With a look of disgust for the reluctant doctors, he went into the room himself, taking medicines and clean clothes to the sick and the dying.

When the epidemic had worn itself out and Egypt was calm again, the Egyptian press praised the young Frenchman and the government gave him a decoration.

"The young French consul," said the Egyptian newspaper, "has shown courage and devotion worthy of his colors. Energetic, tireless, sometimes foolhardy, he has been concerned to see everything for himself; bending over the beds of the dying, he has questioned, consoled and succoured."

Energetic, tireless and foolhardy—these were the characteristics that would always distinguish him and that were essential for the great accomplishment that came later.

France made him a Chevalier of the Legion of Honor for his work throughout the epidemic and even the British minister told the guests at a public banquet in De Lesseps' honor that he had "never seen one so young represent his country more creditably. France is to be congratulated on having men of the stamp of De Lesseps in her service."

Ferdinand was not yet thirty years old. He had not forgotten his Uncle Barthélemy's teaching: "Remember the world is your home, but France is your love." That would be his motto forever.

His natural love for people made him understand those of all stations, even including the viceroy himself, who was no simple personality.

Mehemet Ali was then engaged in extending Egyptian territory by conquest, in the hope that he could eventually pull away from the Ottoman Empire and Turkish rule, bringing Egypt to a state of independence. He had manned his Egyptian galleys with young men from Bethlehem and sent them to Syria on an invasion expedition. Not only Bethlehem, but the whole Christian world protested against this conscription of Christian youth for the fighting of heathen battles. Finally the young men's parents came to Alexandria and appealed to De Lesseps to help them. But when the vice consul suggested the Palestinian youths be sent home, Mehemet Ali refused to listen. He was fighting a war, he insisted, and the galleys had to be manned by some means or other. Palestine was under Egyptian rule. There was nothing else he could do, if he wanted to win the Syrian war. Finally De Lesseps persuaded him to consent to send a few of the boys home —say five a week. That would still keep the galleys going and yet would ease the tension in Bethlehem. But he was mistaken about that. When the women of Bethlehem saw a few of their men coming home, while their own sons and husbands were still enslaved, the uproar was louder than ever. Soon the French vice consul's life was being made miserable by the petitioners.

One morning Ferdinand went to the palace in clothes

that were ragged and torn, flapping tatters of shirt and coat, completely unlike his usual immaculate grooming. The viceroy looked at him in astonishment. Surely he must have met with some horrible accident on his way to the palace.

"What has happened? Who did this to you, Ferdinand?" asked the pasha.

"You, sir," answered De Lesseps sadly.

"I?"

De Lesseps nodded. "Yes. The clutching hands of the petitioners from Bethlehem have finally reduced me to this state. And it is all your fault. I will never see an end to this misfortune so long as you refuse to release more than five conscripts a week."

It was the kind of humor the pasha enjoyed. He threw back his head and roared, his huge body shaking.

"But we can't have this," he declared, at last. "We shall have to send the poor fellows home to Bethlehem while you still have clothes on your body."

Ferdinand stayed in Egypt six years—twice as long as his usual tour of duty. But he was granted a leave of absence to go home on vacation at the end of three years. It was the most important vacation he ever took.

CHAPTER SIX

WHEN FERDINAND returned to Paris, he found all his friends eager to make his vacation gay and exciting. He had a genius for friendship, was warm and charming and witty, and he brought news from the Mediterranean countries. He spent two weeks in Paris, a petted good-natured young bachelor of thirty, browned by the Egyptian sun, full of stories of the pasha and his court and his thirteen sons.

At the end of two weeks, he went to Angers to visit his mother. It amused him that she felt concern for him because of his single state, but he did not know that at last she had decided quietly to do something about it.

Madame de Lesseps, of the noble Spanish family of Montijo, had a neighbor of whom she was very fond, Madame Delamalle. Madame Delamalle's husband was an attorney, and they had a daughter of eighteen named Agathe. Ferdinand's mother was exceedingly fond of the young girl, and she talked to her often and at length about her brilliant son in Egypt. Also, as French mothers will, the two mothers discussed the possibility of a match between the De Lesseps son and the Delamalle daughter. At least, they would see to it that they met, and would hope for the best—that best, as they planned it, being that the two young people would be friends, enjoying occasional correspondence during Ferdinand's absence, until Agathe was old enough to think about marriage and until Ferdinand could again be home on leave.

However, their plans moved forward much faster than they had anticipated. Ferdinand had a way of increasing the tempo of any events that concerned him. Agathe appeared, quite by chance, in the De Lesseps' drawing room and was introduced to the distinguished son. From that moment, she was under the spell of his charm. And he became even more charming, more witty, more fascinating than usual.

After only a few days—his leave was drawing to a close and he had not much time left—he asked her to marry him. He wanted to take her back with him to Egypt. And she was as eager to go as he was to have her with him. But her parents discouraged such impatience. Agathe was too young to go so far away from home so quickly. Give her time to grow up, Madame Delamalle insisted, and she would be all the better wife as a consequence. He was twelve years older than she was. She must be sure of her own heart. If it was really love, it would be all the stronger for waiting.

Reluctantly Ferdinand went back to Egypt without her. He could but recognize the wisdom of his future mother-in-law's arguments. For two years he and Agathe knew each other only from letters. And then once again the vice consul was granted leave—leave to go home for his wedding. They were married on the twenty-first of December, 1837. And De Lesseps was to find that not only had he married an extraordinary wife, but an extraordinary mother-in-law as well. Madame Delamalle proved to be the best friend he had ever known.

From Egypt, the De Lesseps went to Barcelona, Spain, the native country of Ferdinand's mother. They arrived just in time for the Carlist revolution. It was a time of great diplomatic delicacy, with France and England, as usual, taking opposite sides in the political battle. De Lesseps, recalling one of Talleyrand's lessons, that a foreign diplomat represents his country, and not merely this or that political party, refused to take sides in the Spanish trouble, and even when tempers grew hot and a shooting war became inevitable, his answer to the French and English demands that he say which side he was on, was always the same. "I am for an Anglo-French alliance."

It was a time that could have been critical for any new marriage. The embassy was situated halfway between the headquarters of the two warring factions, and directly in their line of fire. Many a twenty-year-old bride, hearing the firing outside her window, would have packed up and gone home to mother. De Lesseps had urged Agathe to do this, but she had insisted that she belonged by his side. Had it been possible for her to have been beside him throughout the shooting, it might not have been quite as hard. But most of the time, his duties made it necessary for her to face danger alone.

There were many French nationalists in Barcelona who must be protected from Spanish fire. It was necessary for De Lesseps to go through the streets that were under fire, guiding civilians to places of safety. The guns must have sounded very close, and very loud and frightening in his absence. Nor could the young bride ever be certain that her husband would return. De Lesseps had ordered a French battleship to be waiting off the coast, ready to sail to France at his order. Into it went all the French nationalists in Barcelona. And even a few frightened Spanish citizens found haven under the French flag.

But Agathe refused the safety of the vessel, so long as her husband stayed in the city. Undoubtedly she was frightened. She had never seen such horrors before. But she was outwardly calm, and her courage delighted Ferdinand. When it was over, both of them wrote to Madame Delamalle about it, each praising the other's bravery. The experience had actually brought them closer together than ever.

Ferdinand said in his letter to Agathe's mother:

"Your dear Agathe is a pearl among women. I do assure you that I have fully appreciated her character and sense during these difficult conditions where it was necessary for me to have all my wits about me, and where I could by no means have been assured of my freedom of action had I a wife like most of those I see here." (After all, it was the badly frightened wives who brought their fears to him. Those who were as brave as Agathe did not come to the embassy.) "She has borne most heroically the trials which we have had to undergo. I have admired her resignation and cheerfulness in circumstances where I have been forced to leave her in order to carry out my duties which have exposed me to great dangers. She has never said anything, nor allowed any emotion to show that might deter me from what I had to do."

This must have been harder for her than her husband realized, for De Lesseps had a way of plunging headlong into dangers, as though he were wading into the ocean for an invigorating swim. Or perhaps this very quality made it easier. She had the same confidence that he would return that she might have had that he would not be drowned in swimming.

Nor was Agathe less proud of her husband. She wrote: "This revolution has shown how fine he is. Everyone loves and admires him. They all say it is due to him there has been no bombardment as yet. The authorities trust him; whatever he asks of the new Junta is granted him. Whenever he appears, they say, 'The consul of France!' And everyone makes room for him."

Madame Delamalle must have smiled when she read

CHAPTER SEVEN

DE LESSEPS' assignment to a special mission to Rome came
to him almost by accident. And an unhappy accident
it was to prove to be. Once more France's unstable government had dethroned a king and elected a president in
1848, when Louis Napoleon was made President of the
Second Republic.

Once again the change in government brought French
foreign officers back home for instructions and reappoint-
ments. Upon his arrival in Paris, De Lesseps went directly
to the Foreign Office to announce his arrival. It was late
winter, but the Paris sunlight seemed to hold the promise
of spring. It was good to be home again, even though the
air was colder than when he had left Spain.

He learned at the Foreign Office that the foreign minister was at the General Assembly, for disturbing news
had just arrived from Rome. De Lesseps decided to go
find him there. It would seem good once again to hear
the debates of the General Assembly. Especially since this
one promised to be rather exciting.

After Napoleon's conquests in Italy, the country had
been divided into small republics. This was not of Napoleon's planning. Under Napoleon, Rome itself had been
a part of the French Empire.

But now Rome was a republic, only lately taken over

by a group of revolutionists under a triumvirate. The Pope had been banished to Gaeta, under Austrian rule, since the revolutionists had no intention of sharing their conquest with the Vatican.

But France did not want to see Austria shielding the Pope of Rome. In fact, she did not want Austria interfering in Italy at all. She might be divided over whether to approve the new Roman Republic or Carlo Alberto's plans for uniting all Italy, but she was completely united in wanting Austria out of Italy. So when Carlo Alberto's plans failed, with Austria victorious, she sent into Italy a contingent of French troops just to sit outside Rome and watch developments. These troops, who declared themselves friendly, sent only to protect Italy from the Austrians, were under the command of General Oudinot.

Mazzini, the revolutionist, had no more desire for French troops than he had for Austrian troops on Italian soil. He had ordered the troops to leave. Instead, General Oudinot, on his own initiative, but with the tacit consent of his country, had marched into Rome to try to take the city, but his troops were met with such opposition, not only from the Republican army but from Roman citizens fighting to save their homes, that he had been forced to retreat. This was the news the Assembly was hearing. What was to be France's next move in a situation that was certainly delicate?

There had been all sorts of suggestions, both wise and foolish, but no decision, when De Lesseps sat down in the Visitor's Gallery. One of the members of the Assembly had noticed his arrival, and the sight of the count's smiling face gave him an idea. Perhaps this man De Lesseps could go to Rome and get a peaceful settlement out of the situation. He addressed the Assembly, suggesting the idea to the members.

"If we dispatch to Rome, without creating any crisis at home, a man upon whom we can rely, I feel convinced the matter can be arranged," suggested M. Senard. "I do not mean to say that the count is a fervid republican, but he has always served his country well abroad, without concerning himself with home politics. If he accepts a mission, he will carry it out faithfully."

Glad of any promise of a solution, the Assembly agreed with M. Senard, and in a few hours, the foreign minister was asking the newly arrived consul once again to leave his country. It was exactly the kind of thing De Lesseps liked best—political maneuvering for keeping peace and avoiding war. When asked to accept, he answered heartily:

"If necessary, I could leave within the hour."

Fortunately such haste was not necessary. Yet it was only a few days before he was given instructions which seemed to him general and vague. He was instructed "at once to deliver the States of the Church from the anarchy that prevails in them and to insure that the reestablishment of the regular power is not darkened, not to say imperilled, in the future by reactionary fury."

He was also to "avoid allowing the men at present invested with power in the Roman States to suppose that we regard them as the regular Government, for that would give them a moral force which they are at present lacking."

Louis Napoleon read the orders himself when De Lesseps went to say good-bye. "Your instructions seem vague and contradictory, sir," he remarked. De Lesseps said nothing, though privately he agreed. But it seemed to him that this very vagueness might be good. It left him free to act as seemed best when the time came.

The story of what happened in Rome is the story of a government trying to be on all sides of a ticklish situation at the same time. France had simply not made up her mind which way she should jump. While allowing De Lesseps to carry on negotiations with the revolutionists, the government was at the same time sanctioning certain other secret negotiations under General Oudinot that were exactly the opposite of those De Lesseps thought he was procuring. And just when De Lesseps believed he had found a peaceful compromise, he received a terse message from his home office.

"Come home at once."

France had at last decided. De Lesseps had merely been playing a delaying action. And now it had come to the point where it must mean either France's honor or his. And he was expendable for France. He was accused of having been far too friendly with the revolutionists, of having disobeyed his country's instructions. He was to be tried for disobedience. In the trial, his accusers brought from the files of the Foreign Office instructions alleged to have been given him upon his departure, in which the necessary items had been written in after he had left for Rome, to substantiate the charge of disobedience. They were not in his original orders.

He knew what it all meant. He would be demoted and all the rest of his life he would be serving miserable stations, with no hope for advancement. In his anger, he offered his resignation. But the speed with which it was accepted surprised him. The sooner the trouble was over and done with, the better.

But it left him, at the age of forty, with no occupation. The only calling for which he was trained had been taken from him. He had given his life in the service of France and France had betrayed him. The disillusionment was worse than the disgrace. It left him drained and empty and without ambition to be otherwise.

Agathe stayed beside him through the long trials in the hot weather. Madame Delamalle tried to help him find himself in some other occupation. She turned over to him the management of her estate near Berry. But he found no joy in his new work, for it seemed to him that it had been given him out of charity.

"I am worthless, ma belle-mère. Only a pensioner on your bounty!" Yet he worked on, dividing the property into small model farms.

To Agathe it seemed the wrong work for him. "One cannot turn a diplomat into a farmer," she told herself. "It is like trying to turn a silk purse into a pig's ear."

One evening she saw him eagerly devouring the foreign news in the papers and then suddenly breathing a long sigh and letting the paper fall to his lap. Quietly she went over, took the paper away from him and brought him his hat.

"Come walk with me," she said. "It has been a long while since we last walked together by the river."

She had remembered his fascination for rivers. He looked upon them as roads, methods of travel from one place to another, trade routes and paths of migration. In every country in which they had lived, he had asked the same questions of every river.

"Where does it go? And where has it come from? Who lives along the route it has travelled?"

Agathe began to talk to him about rivers and oceans. Why hadn't she thought of this before? The old canal! The canal Herodotus describes, that once joined the Nile and the sea.

"Ferdinand, there is no reason why you must feel as you do—that your whole life is finished. You are a young man still. You could have a future even more brilliant than your past."

"Foolish one, you should know better than that. At what calling would you suggest I find this most brilliant future?"

She did not answer at once. They walked beside the Seine and watched the lights go on in the deepening twilight. She offered a silent prayer that the words she would say now would be the right words for this man she loved.

"Remember, in Egypt, the old canal? How you used to have me ride with you, looking for the old walls? I never saw you so excited as over the possibility of a canal across Suez. Wouldn't there be some way you could convince someone that such a canal should be built? Once you had plans and drawings. Couldn't you work on them again? I think I can find them for you."

He looked at her quickly but did not answer. Suddenly his step was more brisk and he held his head higher and a hint of his old sprightliness seemed to come back to him. His hand on Agathe's arm drew her closer.

At last he spoke. "You are truly my guardian angel. But of course. Why have I been so blind? For the first time in my life, I have the leisure to work on those plans. Why have I not done so sooner?"

He was different after that, busy with his books and his papers, writing hundreds of letters to engineers all over the world, rereading the ancient books that told of a canal that united the Nile and the sea.

He had them almost in order for presentation when the worst blow of all—the worst blow that could ever strike him—suddenly fell on him.

CHAPTER EIGHT

IN EARLY fall the family came back to Paris from the summer in the country, to put the children in school. One day soon after school had started, the youngest boy came home with flaming cheeks and a high temperature. Agathe put him to bed and sent for the family doctor. It was scarlet fever. Within a fortnight, the boy was dead.

Agathe and Ferdinand turned to each other in their grief. The sorrow they saw in each other's faces drew them even closer in affection and understanding.

A few weeks later, Charles, the oldest son, grew ill with the same disease. Once again Agathe watched by a child's bedside, night and day. This time the watching was all the harder, for it was tinged with fear. Charles must not be permitted to follow his younger brother! The same nurse who had helped her with the other child came again; they took turns watching and waiting. But Charles turned always to his mother and often refused to allow the nurse to help.

"You are wearing yourself out," Ferdinand told Agathe, noting the dark circles under her eyes. He wondered how long it had been since she had slept through one night. She smiled and patted his arm and shook her head.

"I'm all right. He wants me. He will not take his medicine from anyone else, and he must have the medicine."

But her husband thought he knew why her mouth seemed tight and drawn and why there was a strange look in her blue eyes. "Agathe," he said, taking her hand in his, "because we have lost one son is no reason for you to allow yourself to imagine that it might happen again. That fear, more than Charles' illness, is making you look and feel so exhausted. You must rest, and cease worrying, if you would have strength when you will need it most—when the fever is gone and Charles is better and needs entertainment."

"I know," she said, dropping a kiss on his cheek as she turned to go back to the sickroom. "The doctor says he sees some improvement even now. I want it to continue."

Soon the fever was gone. The bright flush changed to pallor. Charles slept and ate and played with his tin soldiers on the counterpane. His father sat by his bed and told him wonderful stories of Egypt and Barcelona.

One morning at breakfast Ferdinand noticed Agathe's hand tremble a little as she poured his coffee. Then he looked at her face, and felt fear such as he had never known before.

"Do you—feel as well as you usually do, chérie?" he asked.

"I feel like the hottest day of an Egyptian summer."

She rubbed her hand over a flushed cheek. "Why? Do I look different?"

"You look as though you had stood too long in that Egyptian sun." He got up and gathered her into his arms. "I am taking you to bed and calling the doctor. Unless I am badly mistaken, you, too, have the fever."

"She will be all right, Doctor?" he asked when his own diagnosis had been confirmed.

The doctor looked concerned. "She could be better. She has lost sleep. She has felt grief. She can't have too much strength left."

"But enough—enough to see her through?" Ferdinand searched the doctor's face for reassurance. He himself knew nothing of illness. "She'll be all right? Have you—have you left medicine?"

"It is still too soon to know," answered the doctor.

The knowledge came all too quickly. There were complications and Agathe grew weaker as her temperature rose higher and higher. Ferdinand stayed by her bedside, talking to her when she felt like listening, but often just sitting, watching her and praying fervently for her recovery.

One day when her fever was down for a brief time, she smiled at him and reached for his hand.

"What about the canal?" she asked. "Have you sent the new plans to the sultan?"

It was like her to think of him, rather than herself.

He gripped her arm as he answered her, smiling. "The Nile and the Mediterranean and the Red Sea are now holding hands—at least on my papers. The complete plans will be ready to send soon. You must get well quickly, Agathe. Who knows how soon we will be summoned to Suez to build our canal?"

She smiled and said nothing. Then, after a long silence, she said softly, "Talk about Egypt, Ferdinand."

He talked until she fell asleep, recalling the things they had done in those happiest first years of their marriage. Then he sat watching her shallow breathing, with tears in his eyes, wishing those days might be repeated.

Still he was not prepared when it happened. He could not accept her loss. Losing her, he had nothing. He had lost all that meant life to him—his wife, his son, and his work. Both he and Agathe's mother had felt that in spite of the seriousness of her sickness, Agathe would recover. She was so young, and life stretched so far before her. It couldn't end this way.

When it was all over, the wise and tender Madame Delamalle turned Ferdinand's attention once more to Berry, and he found the hard physical work of farming and carpentry an anesthetic for his pain. Yet it worried him, too, that he and his boys were dependent upon Madame Delamalle.

"It hurts me to be on your bounty," he told her. "I

should be making a living for my children. Surely things will have to change soon. I sent the canal plans to the sultan."

He watched the mails closely, and when a large packet came for him, he broke the seal quickly. The canal papers! But when he opened the packet, his hopes died. With them was a formal note from the sultan.

"I am returning the plans you sent me regarding an interoceanic canal to be built in Egypt. Any such project does not seem feasible at this time. Turkey cannot grant you concession to land in Egypt!"

Every man has his own capacity for trouble. When disappointments overflow that measure, the man breaks. Madame Delamalle watched her genial son-in-law change into a depressed and hopeless figure. This had been the one blow too many.

"The canal has been Agathe's idea more than mine, really," he told her. "It is as though they had insulted her with their refusal. I cannot bear that."

Madame Delamalle understood him. "Ferdinand," she said, "for fifteen years I have regarded you as my own son. A better son I could not have wished. Would I not ask my son to help me by becoming my land agent? Would he have felt I was offering him charity? Now I am asking that you have the Agnes Sorel house, La Chesnaye, ready for us to move into by the time the boys' summer vacation starts. Charles will need sunshine and country air after his winter's illness. You can find work for them to do there."

He tried to lose himself in his work. There were so many things he must learn to let go from his consciousness. He did the hardest kinds of manual labor all summer, feeling the good clean pain of tired muscles and aching back.

He decided to send the plans this time to Egypt. He wrote to the Dutch consul in Alexandria and asked him to present them to Mehemet Ali's successor, Abbas Pasha. Once again they came back to him. Abbas Pasha was not interested in any more internal improvements. Egypt had long ago decided not to build such a canal. Why should they change their minds now? De Lesseps thought he knew several reasons—the fact that it had been proved the canal could be built at tide level, that the oceans did not have different tide levels, after all; there were now new ways of building canals; any number of reasons— not to mention the more important one—the great good to the world such a canal would prove to be.

"It will be built someday," he told Madame Delamalle. In his own heart he still hoped that he would be the one who would build it. So long as he had that dream to sustain him, he could keep living.

One morning as he sat on the roof of the house he was rebuilding, nailing new shingles to the old roof, he heard the tinkle of the postman's bell. He called to a workman to bring the mail to him, and went on nailing shingles. The workman dropped the papers and letters over the edge of the roof for him. De Lesseps sat cross-legged on the roof, ripping the envelopes with a nail. One of the letters was sealed with the royal seal of Egypt. He read it through and got up hastily, stuffing the others in his pocket. He climbed down and stood on the ground and said to his foreman, "I must go to Paris. Important news in this mail."

He galloped his horse all the way to Paris. He must tell Madame Delamalle. At home he went from room to room, calling to her.

When she finally heard him and came, he smiled as he used to smile, before his wife's death. It had been a long while since she had seen that smile.

"Madame, at last you are getting rid of your pensioner. You no longer need to put up with me. You will never guess what has happened."

"You have found some jewels hidden away by Agnes Sorel, some jewels given her by King Charles?"

"Better than that. My old friend, the little fat boy Mehemet Said, is the new viceroy of Egypt. I know he will be interested in our canal. I myself taught him to have such an interest. Someday, ma belle-mère—and soon now—our dream will come true."

Gone were all signs of grief and discouragement. He was looking brightly into the future with happy expectancy.

"I shall write Said at once," he said, sitting down at his desk and hunting for pen and paper.

"Tell him you are no longer in foreign service," suggested his mother-in-law. "He will be needing good diplomats, will he not?"

"God is at last on my side, ma belle-mère!" he exulted. "Now my canal will be built at last! Who would have thought of Said being viceroy? Though he will make a good one. He has a bright mind—bright, but not brilliant. I know he will be interested in my canal!"

He began to write, then looked up from his paper. "I shall remind him of the macaroni I used to feed him. I wonder if any man has ever been more pleased by the good fortune of another!"

CHAPTER NINE

THAT LETTER which Ferdinand de Lesseps wrote to his old pupil, Said Pasha, is probably the only letter in history that resulted in the building of a great interoceanic canal. In that respect, at least, it might be judged as De Lesseps' greatest diplomatic achievement.

The answer came as promptly as possible, considering that it had to be brought from Egypt by camel. His old friend Said wrote a warm and friendly letter, inviting Ferdinand to come to Egypt at once. The letter quickly changed De Lesseps' whole outlook. His depression fell from him like a discarded garment. He was again full of plans, making eager arrangements for the voyage.

"I would rather be going to Egypt than anywhere. There Agathe and I were happy. A strange country, ma belle-mère, in which nothing seems to die," he told Madame Delamalle.

Two years before, at the time he first sent his canal plans to Abbas Pasha, Said Pasha's predecessor, De Lesseps had written his friend, Ruyssenaers, consul-general of Holland in Egypt, about his great idea. At that time he wrote:

"I confess that my scheme is still in the clouds, and I do not conceal from myself that, as long as I am the only person who believes it to be possible, that is tantamount to saying it is impossible. What is wanting to make it acceptable to the public is a basis of some kind, and it is in order to obtain this basis that I seek your co-operation . . .

"I send you a memorandum which embodies my ancient and more recent studies, and I have had it translated into Arabic . . . You will form your own opinion as to whether the present Viceroy Abbas Pasha is the man to comprehend the benefit which this scheme would confer upon Egypt, and whether he would be disposed to aid in carrying it out."

Now that he was about to leave for Egypt, he wrote to his friend again, announcing his coming. "Do not say a word about the piercing of the isthmus before I arrive."

He wanted to tell Said about the project himself. He wanted to watch his pupil's face while he told it. He remembered how plainly the boy showed in his face every mood and emotion, every thought and fancy. He would know by that face when the right time came for the great announcement that would mean glory and power for Egypt and greater wealth to the world.

He was not prepared for the reception which met him at Alexandria. The Dutch consul-general and two of the pasha's aides met him. From the very first moment, he was made a member of the viceroy's household. The favors shown him delighted him, for he had suffered from lack of self-esteem ever since his resignation from the Foreign Office. Now he was again treated with pomp and circumstance and no one loved pomp and circumstance more than he. The letters he wrote home to Madame Dellamalle recorded each delicious detail.

"The steamer *Lycurge* landed me at eight this morning at Alexandria. My good friend Ruyssenaers and the Minister of Marine, Hafouz Pasha, came to greet me on behalf of the viceroy and I proceeded in a court carriage to one of His Majesty's villas . . ."

He described the villa, which faced the Mahoudin Canal, the canal that had been built by Said's father, Mehemet Ali. De Lesseps remembered watching the villa being built, when he was in Egypt twenty years before. Never had he dreamed that he would one day be living in it.

It was a luxurious house, with the large reception room and the dining room on the ground floor, and a bright, sunny drawing room, with four rich divans running along its four walls and four large windows looking out on two avenues were above the divans. Oriental houses are usually sparsely furnished. The divans took the place of chairs and sofas and tables. Men drank their morning coffee, and their afternoon and evening coffee as well, sitting beside one another on a divan, discussing politics or women or horses or war. They read while lying on their backs on a divan, or they sat cross-legged, gossiping, while a servant poured them cup after cup of thick coffee.

Off the drawing room was De Lesseps' bedroom, its enormous, luxurious bed hung with yellow silk, embroidered with red flowers and a heavy gold fringe. At night the yellow silk was drawn back, revealing inner curtains of figured tulle designed to keep out the insects while one slept. There was marble furniture in the dressing room, and soft towels embroidered with gold.

He lost no time in making himself quite at home in all this luxury. Said sent a few of his closest friends to welcome his former tutor, and Ferdinand questioned them closely for news of his old friend, eager to gain any possible information about Said's likes and dislikes. The more he knew, the better he would know how to approach the viceroy to get approval of the canal plans. For by that time, the canal had become almost an obsession with him. Fond as were his recollections of his former pupil, it was actually the canal project that had brought him to Egypt.

He learned from his visitors that the viceroy would see him formally at eleven o'clock. Because his old relations with the young prince had been most informal, he decided that it would be advisable for him to appear in court clothes, with his breast decorated with all his old medals and ribbons, even though he was no longer in the French Foreign Service. But Said would like the implied compliment of full dress. When Ferdinand saw his reflection in the mirror, he felt as though he had come home again after a long absence. It was like the old days.

He was back in his own familiar world at last! In Egypt he had been happy.

Said Pasha brushed aside all formalities and received his visitor as an old and dear friend. Coffee was brought and they sat side by side, talking and talking, laughing at old jokes, recalling old memories.

"Have the years since we were together been good to you, Your Highness, or evil?" asked Ferdinand.

"Evil, for the most part," answered Said. "But now that is over, I wish to help Egypt find her proper place among the nations of the world. And I have hoped that you might help me to do this, mon ami." Said smiled.

De Lesseps was secretly certain that he could do just that. But it did not seem to him that the time was right to mention the plan by which it could be best accomplished. "Providence must have reason for placing a prince who has been so carefully educated in his youth and so cruelly tried in his maturity at the head of the most absolute government in the world, Your Highness," he answered. "What Said says, that will Egypt accomplish."

Said did not deny this. De Lesseps watched the viceroy closely as the younger man leaned against the crimson cushions of the divan, his gold-colored fez slightly askew on his dark curly head.

"I sent for you, mon ami," continued the viceroy, "because a ruler can trust few people. I need an advisor whom I can fully trust. I need you, Ferdinand."

De Lesseps felt deeply touched by the younger man's confidence in him. He determined he would never do anything at any time to cause him to lose it.

Said half closed his eyes and straightened his fez as he waited. Finally De Lesseps said, in a tone that was almost an oath of allegiance:

"I shall be honored to serve you, sire. And may you never regret that you asked for my service!" He dropped to one knee in front of the viceroy and offered his sword as a sign of vassalage.

Said laughed. "No, no. Oh, no!" he cried. "You do not kneel to me. You are my good friend from France. You do not serve me, you are to teach me."

They talked again as old friends renewing their friendship. Soon Said seemed drowsy.

"I go to Cairo in a few days, Ferdinand. I must appear before the people of my second capital. We go through the desert, with my troops. Will you go with us, or wait for us to return to Alexandria?"

De Lesseps rubbed his ear. Could he be hearing right? What more perfect opportunity could there be to follow the path his canal would take, across the desert to Cairo?

He looked at the viceroy, smiling. "Do you think I have grown so soft and lazy since I left Egypt that I can no longer stand a few days in the saddle? If you thought that, you are mistaken. Give me a horse and I shall go with you."

He went back to his villa that night, happier than he

had been for years. The heavy scent of mimosa filled the soft air. He thought of Agathe. He was humming a Turkish tune he had heard at the palace. It seemed to him that now Agathe walked beside him. For here in Egypt, did not death seem non-existent? The cradle of the world, Egypt—not its tomb!

The next morning a groom knocked on his door.

"His Highness has sent his good friend this horse, which he has but recently purchased by his own choice in Arabia. You will ride him on our trip to Cairo. But first you had better see how you get on with him. His Highness will ride with you this morning at eleven."

CHAPTER TEN

FERDINAND had decided before he left France that he would wait for a propitious time before mentioning his plan for an Egyptian canal to the viceroy. He knew that proper timing would mean much toward getting Said's approval. But now that he was on the spot where the canal would be built—*he hoped*—it was not easy to keep his secret hidden. Things were happening so rapidly— the viceroy's welcome, his position as royal advisor, and now this trip that would allow him to see again the old walls of the ancient canal. It seemed to him that Destiny was playing a part in his affairs and he must be sure that he knew when and where he was to be led.

He had brought his papers and drawings along on the trip. He hoped to check their accuracy if the chance offered—to make sure that the geographical and geological facts, at least, were as he believed them to be. The mathematical findings, the actual blue prints, would have to come later when the project had been actually approved.

His own enthusiasm soon became greater than his discretion. Before he quite realized what he was doing, he found himself telling his travelling companion, Zulkifer Pasha, one of the viceroy's older brothers, about the work he had done and the information he had gathered together and the hopes he had for a new trade route to India. He had the gift of making others take fire from the spark of his own enthusiastic faith, and even in that first day of travel, he had won a follower in the person of Zulkifer Pasha. He, too, saw that such an undertaking would indeed make Egypt great in the eyes of the world both east and west of Suez.

"Think what it would mean to the future!" cried De Lesseps. "A direct route to Mecca for the Mohammedans and a shorter distance to India for Europe. How can I interest your brother?"

"Have you told him?"

"Not yet."

"Then do so. He will listen, I feel sure."

The viceroy had left Alexandria a day earlier than the rest of the royal party. He was riding in a strange kind of carriage that resembled an omnibus but which was fitted up on the inside as a luxurious bedroom. The troops that accompanied him were a royal military escort and they were making double use of the occasion of their ruler's coronation in his second capital by performing their annual maneuvers on the way. It was for this reason that Said had left early.

Arrangements had been made for the others to join him at the first resting place on the way. Before a viceroy goes on a journey, through the desert, he must know where he can safely stop for rest and refreshment along the way.

Though De Lesseps' mind was still boiling with thoughts of his project, he did not mention it, as he and Zulkifer sat with the viceroy in his carriage, drinking coffee, and listening to Said's boasting tales of his generals' horsemanship. Military maneuvers had largely consisted of games on horseback across the desert. There had been both beauty and great skill in them, and Said had enjoyed both, with a feeling of deep pride that these were his own soldiers.

The time was certainly not propitious that evening.

But the morning of the third day found De Lesseps sleepless. He lay on the hard pallet inside his tent, hot and restless. The tent seemed unbearably stuffy, and he got up and went outside to breathe deeply of the cool morning air. Dew was still thick on the grass, but the sun above was already beginning to shine through the morning mist. He looked out over the desert, and suddenly he stood transfixed.

A mammoth rainbow made from dew and dust and fog stretched before him in the distance, its two ends hidden by distant mountains, its broad arc seeming to join earth and heaven. It was an awesome sight, and to De Lesseps it suddenly seemed to have a supernatural meaning. Here was his message from heaven! Here and now was the time most propitious.

He felt deeply moved as he watched the rainbow, for to him it seemed clear that God Himself was directing him now. And with God on his side, how could he fail?

He was merely the instrument of God's intention to bring peace to the world in his time, through the joining of two mighty oceans, the Red Sea and the Mediterranean.

He walked back and forth before his tent, repeating his morning prayers, his mother's rosary twined round his fingers, happy to have found his Christian God in this unchristian country. Yet all the while a part of his mind was concerned with the words he would say to the Egyptian ruler.

This was the day!

It was the fifteenth of November, 1854. He had been eight days in Egypt.

He went as usual to have morning coffee with the viceroy. Zulkifer was there, and another brother, Helim Pasha, and the viceroy's military aides. De Lesseps was pleased to find the viceroy in high good humor. Said was a man of moods, and when his mood was a black one, he would listen to no one. But this morning's good mood, too, was a portent. Heaven had opened the way for a Suez Canal.

Ferdinand went back to his own tent for breakfast, as was his custom, and unpacked his papers. These he took with him when he returned to the viceroy's carriage. Zulkifer was still with his brother, waiting for De Lesseps' return, though he had said nothing to his brother about his friend's intention.

The men sat talking on various subjects. Said was full of patriotic feeling on the eve of his second coronation—

he had already been crowned in Constantinople, as a ruler of the Ottoman Empire—and he talked of Egypt and his dreams for her and for his reign.

"I want my name to go down in history as one who brought Egypt prosperity, rather than war."

De Lesseps caught his breath. Again the intervention of heaven—guiding the conversation so that it furnished an opening for the introduction of his great subject!

"You want your reign to go down in history as one in which Egypt has prospered as never before? You want me to tell you how to do this? Well, I can tell you I know a way."

The viceroy stared at him. Then he pulled his fez down over his eyes, as he was in the habit of doing when thinking or sleeping. De Lesseps began to wonder, after several minutes, which this might be. He looked at Zulkifer who merely raised an eyebrow but said nothing.

"Tell me," said Said, opening one eye. "I listen."

"Do you remember when you were my pupil, how on our rides we would look for the remnants of the ancient canal that joined the Nile to the Red Sea?"

Said pushed his fez back for a moment, then pulled it over his forehead again. "I remember. I have followed the same paths many times."

"That ancient canal was not permanent because it was built wrong. The silt from the Nile piled up and eventually closed it. But cut straight across Suez, as Linant Bey has lately suggested, join the Red Sea with the Mediterranean, provide a lake for the silt to flow through, and you will have shortened the world's shipping routes thousands of miles. Moreover, you would have accomplished something that no one else has ever succeeded in doing! It can be done, Said. Those who say it can't be are ignorant of the facts. If you would build such a canal, your name would be green forever."

The viceroy took his fez off entirely. "I must hear more," he said. "Now tell me."

De Lesseps brought out his papers. He traced the findings of engineers from the time of Napoleon down to the present, as shown by Egypt's own engineer, Linant Bey.

"You see Lapere was wrong. The seas are not of different levels. The canal could be built at sea level. Straight across Suez. It will be practical, and not too expensive to make a good profit. It would be worth far more to you than it could possibly cost, and no one could even estimate its value to the world."

The viceroy studied the maps himself and made his own computations. He went through all the papers, scanning them quickly. Then he leaned back, pulled his fez far over his eyes and sat without moving. Had De Lesseps been less familiar with his attitudes, he might have thought His Highness was sleeping. Finally he pushed back his fez and sat up very straight. He smiled at his new advisor.

"I see it," he said. "I am convinced. I accept your plan, my friend. I, too, believe it can be done. Now we shall

spend the rest of the time on this journey figuring out
how to do it."

Ferdinand could have cried with joy. He grabbed
Said's hand and held to it tightly. He could feel tears
stinging his eyelids. Suddenly he got up from the divan.

"It is too great joy!" he cried hoarsely. "I must leave
you!" He went outside and galloped away on his horse,
jumping the parapet that surrounded the viceroy's entourage to insure its safety.

Said's generals sat in the shade, watching their troops
at rest. They cheered when they saw the Frenchman
jump his horse with all the skill of an Arab. They, too,
were expert horsemen and recognized skill in another.
A man who could ride like that could do almost anything. Any two of them would have agreed on that.

Just before sundown the viceroy called these same
generals into his carriage for a conference. He sent a
messenger for De Lesseps to join them. Ferdinand came,
riding at full speed, again jumping the high parapet
easily. He heard the generals cheer him, and waved a
hand in greeting.

"Tell them, too," ordered the viceroy, "what you told
me this morning."

De Lesseps told the Egyptian generals his conclusions
about the canal. He knew they understood little or nothing of his explanations, for they knew little or nothing
of engineering. Yet when the viceroy asked them: "What
do you think of my friend's proposal to build such a

canal across Suez? Shall we agree to do it?" every man there voted "Yes!" No man could have wrong ideas who was such a superior horseman, they reasoned. But few of them had the imagination to guess what such a canal would mean to Egypt, or to the world.

"Prepare a memorandum of your full plans, to be formally presented to me in Cairo," the viceroy told De Lesseps.

The light burned late in Ferdinand's tent at every relay after that. He had told the servants, soon after his arrival in Egypt, that he would not require a table set with food late at night, but now he changed his order. Coffee and food, and then back to his papers. The memorandum must cover all possible questions. It must answer all possible objections.

The more he worked, the more he began to realize the magnitude of the undertaking. It could well change the whole history of the world. It could even end wars forever. Or cause them, if it were not managed properly. Every country would want the canal to be kept always neutral, however, and always open, and to achieve that, each would refuse to make war on the other. How fortunate that it was to be Egypt and Mehemet Said who would build it!

He reread the memorandum when it was done.

"Camp of Marea
November 15, 1854
"The joining together of the Mediterranean Sea and

the Red Sea by a navigable canal is an enterprise the utility of which has attracted the attention of all great men, who have reigned or been for a time in Egypt: Sesostris, Alexander, Caesar, the Arab conqueror Amrou, Napoleon I and Mohammed Ali. A canal communicating by way of the Nile with the two seas existed in ancient times—but for how long we know not—under the old Egyptian dynasties; during a second period of 445 years, from the first successors of Alexander and the Roman conquest until the fourth century before the Hegira, and finally for a period of 130 years after the Arab conquest."

He told how Napoleon, as soon as he had arrived in Egypt, had appointed a committee to look into the possibility of such a canal. He told of Lapere's report, the very same report he had first read on a quarantined ship when he was a young man in his twenties. He quoted Napoleon's words, when he read Lapere's report. "The work is great, and though I shall not now be able to accomplish it, the Turkish government will someday reap the glory of carrying it out."

Then he began to set out his own project.

"The time has come to realize Napoleon's prediction. The piercing of the Isthmus of Suez is certainly an enterprise destined to contribute more than any other to the maintenance of the Ottoman Empire and to demonstrate to those who announced its approaching ruin that it still has a fruitful existence before it, and that it is capable of

adding a brilliant page the more to the history of civilization."

At the time at which he was writing, Russia had invaded Turkey, in the hope of getting a new port on the
Black Sea, and France and England had formed a hasty
alliance to resist Russia's aggression, the Crimean War.
This same war was later to complicate the politics of the
Suez Canal. Wars were forever being fought over a nation's right to use waterways; surely a seaway open alike
to all nations would prevent wars.

"If the commerce of the world were to pass through
Egypt (through such a canal) the position of the Empire
would be greatly strengthened, for the great European
powers, in order to prevent any one of them from ever
seizing it, would regard it as a vital necessity to maintain
the neutrality of the canal." And then he outlined his
plan.

Linant Bey, Egypt's foremost engineer, who had made
the question of the junction of the two seas his constant
study for thirty years, had proposed to pierce the isthmus
almost on a straight line at its narrowest point, forming
a large inland port in the basin of Lake Timsah and
making the passes of Pelusium and Suez available to ships
of largest tonnage from the Mediterranean and the Red
Sea. It was near the close of the sailing ship era, the
beginning of steamships, which would make the canal
even more useful than De Lesseps had hoped.

The closing paragraphs of the memorandum are characteristic of the man, in their vague and casual reference to the economic necessities of such a tremendous project.

"No operation, however difficult, is now regarded by modern art as impossible. Its feasibility is not doubted; it is merely a question of money, which the spirit of enterprise and co-operation will soon solve, if the profits which are to result from it are in proportion to its cost. It is easy to show that the cost of the Suez Canal, taking the highest estimate, is not out of proportion with the usefulness and the profits of this great work, which would bridge by more than half the distance between the principal countries of Europe, America and the Indies."

The viceroy made some suggestions of changes in the long document, though for the most part he approved it. He had asked De Lesseps also to draw up a firman, a paper granting the concession to build the canal, with the permission of Turkey, who controlled the Ottoman Empire. But the concession was not granted to De Lesseps himself, but to the international company he was to organize, though then non-existent, for the purpose of building the canal.

"So the first thing I must do is to get Turkey's approval of your firman," said De Lesseps, when the documents had all been approved by the viceroy.

"Get the consent of the British consul, Mister Bruce," advised Said. "With your new Anglo-French alliance for the protection of Turkey, that should be easy." He was not at all sure that it *would* be as easy as his words implied. He would find it interesting to watch. He had often wondered just how strong this Anglo-French alliance really was. He would soon know that, at least.

"I shall see Mr. Bruce as soon as we get to Cairo," promised the impatient De Lesseps.

They were finishing their journey on a little Nile steamer. They sat on deck under a brightly striped awning, talking about the canal—always and forever about the canal, with De Lesseps increasing his chief's interest in it hour by hour.

"Where will I find my company? And how start raising money? These things are quite outside my experience. I don't know where to start," De Lesseps admitted.

"You have friends in all countries, have you not, mon ami?" asked the viceroy.

"I have many friends everywhere," Ferdinand answered.

"You have many friends who have money?"

"I have many friends with money and more without."

"It is the ones with money we shall need first; the others—later." The viceroy grinned. "Go out and find yourself one hundred friends—in Egypt, in France, in the world, wherever they may be—a hundred men who trust you enough to risk one thousand dollars in your new enterprise. They will be your first stockholders. From them you can pick the officers of your new company."

It was not as easy as he had thought it would be to

find one hundred men willing to risk their own money in an enterprise about which they knew almost nothing. It took faith and courage, too, to risk even a thousand dollars in so untried a venture. How could they be sure the canal would ever be finished?

"What I start, I finish. I do not give up," he told them. And those who did have the faith and the courage to take so great a risk were to live to see the day when their one thousand dollars became two hundred thousand, and the enterprise itself became the greatest engineering feat ever completed.

Only two weeks in Egypt, and his dream was already beginning to come true. At least it was closer—close enough that he could see it in every detail now. The clouds were becoming transparent.

First, the firman. Once it was obtained, all the other problems would be well on their way to solution, he thought.

"I shall see Mr. Bruce," he told Said, as they sipped their coffee. "If my visit is not a success, then I shall go at once to Constantinople. For then we will need to get to the Turkish prime minister before England reaches him. But I cannot imagine England either refusing to give her permission, or allowing Turkey to give hers. We shall soon see."

CHAPTER ELEVEN

THE HAPPY enthusiasm with which Ferdinand de Lesseps presented his favorite subject to others made it next to impossible for anyone listening not to catch some of his own fire. This often made it seem to him that men were in agreement with him, when, away from the magnetism of his presence and able to think more soberly, they were, at least, skeptical that his great idea was practical. This may to some extent explain why Ferdinand reported to the viceroy that the British consul to Cairo approved of the canal.

De Lesseps reported that Mr. Bruce had virtually given the plan his approval, although of course there had been no time for him to report to his government. But he had gone so far as to admit that he personally could find no objection to the scheme as presented, so long as it was all done by an international company and not by any one nation, and so long as its management would also be international with no special favors to any one country. Since this was exactly De Lesseps' and Said Pasha's idea, there could be no ground for disagreement.

Yet it could have been that the scheme, at that point, seemed so impossible to realize that the British consul scarcely thought it worth his trouble to express doubts and to suggest obstacles for a project that was wholly imaginary and would never be anything else. Such, at least, seemed to be the feeling in London, for on December 18, two weeks after De Lesseps had talked to Mr. Bruce, the London *Times* gave its opinion:

"Notwithstanding the sanguine expectations of M. Lesseps it is generally believed that this undertaking, which will require a capital of fully six million pounds sterling, will not be carried into effect, as, while Europe is engaged in a terrible war (the Crimean) the end of which no one can foresee, it is not likely that many persons will embark their funds in such a project and therefore, like the scheme which was recently entertained, of running steam tugboats on the Nile, it will die a natural death from the want of capitalists to take shares. It is not unlikely that Said Pasha gave his consent so readily because His Highness saw no great probability of the work being ever commenced, and it must also be considered that Said Pasha's assent requires confirmation by the Sultan at Constantinople where political interests may induce the European ministers to advise the Porte to withhold it.

"The great difficulty attending the usefulness of a canal across the Isthmus of Suez lies in the shallowness of the sea to a considerable distance from both the Suez and the Mediterranean shores, and that it is to be cut through a barren desert where not a drop of potable water is to be found. At Suez vessels cannot approach the shore within seven miles so that a canal across the isthmus would be of little use, when the vessels could not reach the mouth of the proposed cut within seven miles of the Red Sea side and four miles on the Mediterranean."

But the London *Times* reporter was evidently not an engineer. Linant Bey, who was an engineer, not only believed it could be done, but was eager to prove it. Yet the words the reporter wrote in his paper did much to form the opinion of his countrymen.

Whatever Mr. Bruce's reasons for his approval, when the viceroy heard his agent's report, he remarked dryly, "I hope you are right."

The following day, Ferdinand received a summons from Said Pasha to come to the citadel palace to a meeting of the foreign consuls. He dressed in his formal court clothes and went to the citadel, still not sure why the meeting had been called, but hoping that it might have something to do with Suez.

When they were assembled, Said Pasha rose and spoke slowly so the interpreters would have time to translate as he talked. He wanted to announce to them, he said, that he had decided to build an oceanic canal across Suez. He was giving his good friend from France, Le Comte Ferdinand de Lesseps, a concession to organize an international company for that purpose. The concession provided that permission must first be obtained from the Supreme Porte which controlled the activities of the Ottoman Empire. Then he turned to his former teacher with a smile.

"Is not this true, my friend? Tell them about it."

Ferdinand lost no time in telling his story to these assembled representatives of most of the nations of Europe and America and Asia. As usual, he carried his audience with him. One after another they all expressed their approval. What a fine thing for the countries they represented! What a wonderful thing for world trade everywhere! The conference ended with every man hurrying back to his consulate to write his report to his government. This was news!

When they had gone, De Lesseps turned to the viceroy, his eyes shining with affection.

"I was forty-nine years old last week," he said. "You have given me the most wonderful birthday present I have ever known."

The viceroy wanted to discuss the meeting. "Did you see Mr. Bruce's expression? He has had no word from his government, not even an acknowledgement of his report. Yet he was the first to hear about our plans. Does England intend to give us trouble?"

"If the others approve, Great Britain will have to," optimistically remarked De Lesseps. "Even the American grinned when you said we would have our canal finished before his American canal joining their two oceans is begun. What rapid progress we are making!"

"Perhaps not as rapid as it might seem," Said warned.

"Turkey's permission will be hard to get without England's. And there can be no canal without Turkey's approval."

"I promise you I will get that approval," vowed De Lesseps. "We will have your firman signed by the Turkish grand vizier or by the sultan himself, if I have to go to Constantinople to get it."

He was to go much, much farther than that before the firman was finally granted. He was to travel more than twenty-five thousand miles by camel and by water before the canal was even started.

On November 30, not yet a month from De Lesseps' arrival in Alexandria, the concession the viceroy granted his agent was signed in Cairo. It was a personal agreement granted to "our friend, M. Ferdinand de Lesseps." He was given exclusive right to organize and manage an internationally owned company which was to be set up for the purpose of cutting through the isthmus and building a canal.

The stockholders of the company were to receive seventy-five per cent of the profits, the Egyptian government fifteen per cent and the founders ten per cent. The project was to be completely removed from any national politics whatever. Toll would be the same for all nations and no nation would be favored above another. The concession was to run for ninety-nine years from the completion of the canal, and at the end of that time it would become the property of Egypt. Work was not to begin until the concession had been ratified by the Supreme Porte.

Getting that ratification was to take most of De Lesseps' time for four years. But before he asked for it, he must give the viceroy assurance that the plan was possible. Therefore, there must first be a complete exploration of the canal site by the engineers chosen to build the canal. Then the Supreme Porte would have no grounds for refusing the firman. The money from the original stockholders—the founders—would pay for the exploration.

The exploring party left Cairo two days before Christmas in 1854.

The two engineers and their assistants, and a group of friends from Cairo who might become stockholders in the new company, went with them. They travelled by camel most of the way, and Ferdinand soon learned that in order to stay on a camel's back when the animal rose from his knees, one must lean far forward, instead of backward to keep one's balance.

In order to have a written record of every impression throughout the journey, he kept an accurate diary. It would be valuable, he had decided, when he talked with men who were not engineers, whose viewpoint would be the same as his own. The journal became largely a record of his own emotional reaction to the events of the trip.

De Lesseps' reactions were usually from the heart first, and then the head.

"The rising sun lights up my room and, opening my windows, I gaze in mute contemplation upon the Red Sea . . . Suez is an isolated point surrounded by deserts; its population, numbering from three to four thousand, is a very miserable one, having only brackish water to drink. Our canal will bring it water and activity, which it lacks . . . I am anxious to see (everything) for myself, as when I have taken in a thing myself, I shall be able to make it comprehensible for those who are not engineers."

The days were spent in exploring, the nights in listening while the engineers explained their computations. Each of the two engineers had his own contribution to make to the expedition. Linant knew the topography of the country, its geology and its geography. He was familiar with the whole canal system of Egypt, knowledge which was of especial value to the new undertakin. Moguel, on the other hand, had built many of the great hydraulic irrigation projects of Egypt and would be able to tell, after studying the whole route, the answer to that question no one as yet could answer—where should the canal be entered, both on the Red Sea and on the Mediterranean?

They spent Christmas Day driving along the canal site, tracing the ancient waterways built by Egyptian pharaohs. Before they had finished their explorations, they had gone from Suez to Shollef to Little Bitter Lake, to Serapeum, to Lake Timsah, to El Quantora to Lake Miselah, to Pelusium which was to be renamed Port Said. The engineers' helpers measured the ancient canal bed, and found its measurements were the same as set down in Herodotus, where they had been recorded millenniums before. Ninety cubits deep, Herodotus had reported it, and though a cubit might vary somewhat, being the distance from finger to elbow, it was usually between eighteen and twenty inches. The canal bed was still ninety cubits.

In late afternoon they returned to their hotel to talk over their findings and Linant's servant served them coffee while they drew the lines the canal would probably take.

The next day they started by small steamer to the Fountain of Moses, which was said to be the first resting place Moses allowed the Children of Israel when they were escaping from Egypt. On their way they were to stop to have breakfast at the first oasis, or spring. Mr. Costa, manager of the hotel there, had prepared a breakfast for the viceroy's official party in which the pièce de résistance was a sheep roasted whole. Mr. Costa met them at the dock and led them proudly into his dining room. Pride rang in his voice as he introduced them to his wife and sister-in-law, both dressed in their oriental best, their faces half veiled, their eyelids and lashes, their cheeks and even their toenails painted. De Lesseps promptly invited them to join the guests from Cairo on the small steamer that waited for them to finish their breakfast. The wind was blowing the red sand—they could see little red whirlwinds in the distance, as they embarked. The farther they went, the higher the waves grew, and now and again the wind almost blew the little boat on its side. The Oriental women were every bit as frightened as the European women whenever this seemed about to happen and they squealed just as loudly and just as futilely.

Practically everyone on board felt relieved when the captain finally announced, "The sea is too rough for landing at the Fountain of Moses. It would be dangerous even to try it. Shall we turn back, my lord?"

"Turn back," agreed Ferdinand. "The roads would be too dusty to travel, even if we could land."

The little steamer chugged back to Suez, and the visitors made their plans to return to Cairo early the following morning. De Lesseps and his men were not sorry to see them go. Now they could get down to work.

That week they examined the Port of Suez foot by foot. At low tide they went out to what they thought were large rocks on some small islands. When they reached the islands, they found the rocks were ancient pieces of masonry. Even on that deserted island, men had once lived and had erected buildings.

"What sort of people and what sort of boats have gone by this spot in past generations?" Ferdinand wrote that night in his journal.

They collected samples of rocks and plants, of sand and water, to take back for analysis. They discovered on the island an old graveyard that had once belonged to the East India Company, which Arab women had evidently robbed, to use the bones of white women as amulets in hope they would ensure their having children as a favor from their ancient gods.

The second night they spent at Suez, they dined with the British consul there, and De Lesseps was once more impressed with what the canal could do for people everywhere, for their meal that night consisted of mutton from Calcutta, potatoes from Bombay, green peas from England, poultry from Egypt, water from the Ganges, wine from France, coffee from Mocha and tea from China, all brought to Suez by an overland carrier.

"Who dares say the world will not come through Suez!" exclaimed Ferdinand happily.

Before another month had passed, they had explored every foot of the way from Suez to Pelusium, planning as they explored, estimating how many gallons of water would flow from the Nile to the Mediterranean when the canal was finished, and how many ships of what size could pass through the canal in how many days and hours, and how much shipping each might be expected to carry, at how much a ton. They guessed at the cost of construction, and tried to decide if any or all or what portion of the old canal could be repaired and used. Then they were ready to listen to Moguel Bey tell them where he thought ships should enter and where they should leave the canal, and where the ships could wait their turn when the canal was crowded. These were things they had to know before the first shovel of earth could be thrown.

When they had enough answers, they went back to Cairo to write their reports for the viceroy. The canal would be about 86 miles long from the Mediterranean to the Red Sea, with a varying width of 328 feet where the banks were low to 190 feet in deep cuttings where they were high. It would be 26 feet deep, with a width of 72 feet at bottom, with a slope of bank near the waterline of one in five and near the base, one in two. The whole channel, it was discovered, could be divided into nine sections. At least several and perhaps all nine of these sections could be in process of construction at the same time. And there need be no locks. The two seas were the same level.

As they pored over these field notes, they began to see the whole thing as it would look when done. The very grandeur of the project silenced them. They could only look at each other in wonder.

"It will be done! It will be done—as I have always known it would be!" murmured De Lesseps.

While he was waiting for the engineer's formal report, which would take several months' preparation, he went to Constantinople.

"Now all that remains is Turkey's approval," he said.

But sometimes the smallest obstacles prove the hardest to surmount. He was to find this true of the firman.

CHAPTER TWELVE

FEBRUARY of 1855 found Ferdinand de Lesseps in Constantinople, planning his diplomatic campaign to persuade Turkey to approve his firman to build a canal across Suez. It was the worst possible time to be asking such a favor, for Turkey was engaged in the Crimean War, in which Russia had invaded Turkey to win for herself an outlet to the Black Sea. Great Britain and France, immediately alarmed by this threat of Russia's, had quickly joined in an alliance of uncertain strength pledging Turkey their combined protection. Turkey, having no navy, welcomed such allies and was certainly in no position to offend either Great Britain or France.

By that time De Lesseps knew that England would never be in favor of what Said Pasha called "your canal business," unless public opinion could be persuaded to change. Constantinople, always a cosmopolitan city, was doubly so in wartime, buzzing with the political intrigues of half a dozen countries. The count did not go directly to the grand vizier. De Lesseps, himself, was familiar with political intrigue. The first few days he spent gathering information, seeing old friends, attending parties, asking questions and listening. One thing he was pleased to learn was that the war had so occupied everyone's time and conversation that there had been no mention of Suez, either for or against. He felt relieved. He could still get to the grand vizier before Great Britain!

Had he been representing France instead of Egypt, he might have been more concerned with the number of British ships in the harbor. However, he was already quite sure that the sultan and his government were completely under the influence of the British in the person of the British ambassador to Turkey, Lord Stratford de Redcliffe.

When he thought the time had come to call on the grand vizier, Reschid Pasha, he took pains to remind him that, though a Frenchman, he was not in any way connected with the French government.

"I am not here as an agent of the French government but as an agent of your good friend, the viceroy of Egypt," he announced.

"That is good," agreed Raschid Pasha.

"I come as a friend of your nation, offering opportunity for greater progress."

When he had finished his story, he saw that Raschid Pasha had been favorably impressed. Such a project would of course be of great value to Turkey. But in the end, the grand vizier remembered his allegiance.

"You understand we are at present in no position to displease our western allies. The British fleet has been of tremendous good to us, making possible our resistance to Russian aggression. I must first consult with Lord Stratford de Redcliffe before I give you my final answer."

"But you will try to persuade him to see what your consent will mean to the whole world?"

Raschid Pasha smiled. "No one, sir, ever persuades Lord Redcliffe to change his mind."

De Lesseps knew this to be true. There was no more bigoted representative of the British crown in all the foreign services than this same Lord Redcliffe who stubbornly refused even to learn the language of the country to which he was sent to serve Britain's interests.

"Let them speak to me in a civilized tongue, if they want me to listen," he was fond of saying. "Let them speak English."

This presented a difficulty to De Lesseps himself, for he spoke English badly and was not always sure that he understood all the innuendoes of diplomatic conversation in that language.

When he finally called upon Lord Stratford de Redcliffe, he felt that their interview left much to be desired. He had written his lordship from Egypt, and when, after his interview with the grand vizier, he had gone to the sultan, he had found that the British diplomat had already seen the sultan. The sultan could do nothing except obey the orders of the British ambassador. Even that first enthusiasm of Raschid Pasha's quickly cooled after a talk with Lord Redcliffe.

"Your Excellency will not allow it to be said," De Lesseps told Lord Redcliffe at their first interview, "that England, which with justice declares she has only drawn the sword against Russia in the interests of civilization, of the freedom of the sea, and of the independence of Turkey, should be the only power to put difficulties in the way of a work that essentially favors the realization of principles which should be the consequence of the Anglo-Austro-French alliance, and which will assure the pacification of the East."

Perhaps even Lord Redcliffe felt the charm of this agreeable Frenchman, for though another meeting had been arranged, he wrote De Lesseps a note, avoiding another encounter.

"In a situation such as mine, personal independence has its limits and cannot but yield at times to official eventualities."

De Lesseps, who always preferred personal independence to official eventualities, saw that he was wasting his time in Constantinople. There was no use staying longer. He must go back to Egypt, and try to persuade the viceroy to allow him to go ahead with forming his company and beginning operations as soon as possible, letting the virtual approval of the grand vizier take the place of his actual signature on the firman. Besides, had not the British engineer, George Stephenson, and his associates built a railroad from Cairo to Suez, without asking or receiving permission from the Supreme Porte? Why then, was it necessary for the viceroy to have such approval?

Disgusted but not discouraged, Count de Lesseps went directly to the palace upon his arrival in Alexandria. He had planned half a dozen opening speeches that would lead to persuading Said Pasha to allow him to go ahead without the firman. The viceroy, he was told upon his arrival at the palace, would see him immediately.

He knew the moment he saw Said Pasha's plump round face mottled with crimson that something had made him exceedingly angry. His gold fez was pulled far down on his forehead. He did not even reply to the greeting from his "good friend from France."

De Lesseps, who knew his moods all too well, was puzzled.

"Have I done something wrong, Your Highness?" he asked. "What is it?"

Said Pasha pushed back his fez an inch or so and squinted at his visitor.

"Not you," he said thickly.

"Who, then? What has happened?"

"You know a man—you've seen a man—Lord Stratford de Redcliffe?" The viceroy seemed threatened with choking.

"The British ambassador to Turkey? What about him?"

"This letter—he wrote me a letter—warning me

against you, my good friend from France. I am not to throw myself into the arms of France."

"But I explained very carefully that I am your agent, Your Highness, not France's."

"He seems not to have understood your abominable English. He even mentions the British fleet—whose duty it is to protect British interests, wherever they may be threatened."

"In Turkey? Or in Egypt?"

"It is a very polite letter. But I believe he means here in Egypt. He mentions that my own father was once deposed. And if I should be so foolish—as to throw myself into the arms of France—"

"You—you—? He has not frightened you? You have not ceased to trust me? You will go on with the project?" De Lesseps anxiously examined the viceroy's expression. He sighed with relief to see a smile.

"More than ever now," answered Said. "I trust you— far more than I trust this Lord Stratford de Redcliffe. But you must still get for me the consent of the Supreme Porte. Without it, your canal would be the center of continual political wrangles."

De Lesseps felt like the prince in the fairy tale, asked to do the impossible in order to gain a boon from his liege lord.

"There is only one way to do that," he said. "We must take the war into the enemy's country."

"You mean?"

"I must go to England at once, Your Highness. I must find out the true reason for England's disapproval. After all, she is the one nation most certain to benefit from such a waterway. Her objections must be much deeper than merely the nationality of Your Highness' agent, or the unfounded British fear that the French government is at this moment on the verge of collapse."

CHAPTER THIRTEEN

DE LESSEPS carefully planned his propaganda campaign before leaving for England. He knew the task would not be an easy one, but he hoped to be able to tell the English people about Suez in a way that would make them no longer allow their country's official rejection of the canal. To accomplish this, certain things must first be done.

He went back to Paris in early spring, for most of the things that he needed to do could be done best in France. He must have the backing—or at least the recommendation—of some reputable financial house. He must make the British press understand the project, so that they would stop printing the pseudo-humorous insults they had been chortling over for months. He must get the approval of prominent men in all the nations of Europe.

He was well endowed and well connected for this diplomatic and political part of his undertaking. The Empress Eugénie, whose maiden name had been Montijo, was his cousin, and she was devoted to him. At her insistence, Emperor Louis Napoleon became interested, and not only promised his support, but time and time again was actually to save the project from failure. De Lesseps' years in foreign service, and his natural disposition for making friends were valuable to him now, also. Soon his friends and relatives were begging to be allowed to have a share in the canal.

The emperor himself arranged for De Lesseps to meet the Paris representative of the London *Times*. And with such an introduction, the newspaper man listened attentively to De Lesseps, and, even as so many others, ended by believing. He sent back a story for his paper which appeared just a few days before De Lesseps himself crossed the Channel. Part of that London *Times'* story was, in a way, apology for the earlier humor that had appeared in that paper.

"The project for cutting a canal through the Isthmus of Suez begins to occupy so much of the attention of the public, notwithstanding the absorbing interest attached to our operations in the Crimea, that it may not be considered out of place to say a few words . . . The terms of the firman exclude the idea that has been entertained that the said concession was exclusively granted to a single French subject, or even to a French company. It was granted to an association of shareholders of every country, to be constituted by the person already named as representative or negotiator of the Viceroy . . ."

From the emperor also, the viceroy's negotiator received letters of introduction to both the Rothschild and Baring banking houses. De Lesseps had known one of the Rothschild brothers in Spain, and when he went to call on the firm in Paris, he found himself received most cordially. Indeed, the firm seemed quite eager to handle the business affairs of the stock-selling end of the project.

Ferdinand de Lesseps was certainly no financial wizard, and he was no engineer, yet he presumed to embark on a project that required the highest possible skill in both fields. Certainly some special genius must have guided him. But his inexperience was plain to be seen in financial matters. He himself told the story of his visit to Rothschild & Company, international bankers.

He had explained to the bankers his plan for international subscriptions to Suez Canal stock, and they had approved of the idea, and had offered the services of their bank for issuing and distributing the stock. It seemed that all arrangements for financing the project had been completed. Then, quite casually, De Lesseps had asked:

"And what do you wish in exchange for your services?"

The bankers had looked at him, almost in unbelief. How could anyone be so naive?

"It's easy to see you're not a business man," remarked one of the brothers, in a shocked voice. "It will be the usual five per cent."

Though not a business man, Ferdinand was able to figure quickly what five per cent of two hundred million francs would be. He looked about him at the shabby old bank building.

"You mean you would take ten million francs away

from my stockholders, just for the privilege of using these dingy corridors? No, thank you. Keep your bank. We will make the issue without you. I will hire an office for which I will pay twelve thousand francs a month. It will answer."

"You will never succeed if you do that," the bankers assured him. "You will need us, if the public are to have confidence in your enterprise." Yet that is exactly the way he did it.

"We shall see," he answered.

He explained his own thinking on the subject of finances—this man who was no business man—to one of the executives of his international company in a letter.

"You ask me upon what basis I propose to place the financial part of the company. I have, upon that point, only one principle, very firmly fixed, it is true, but the means for carrying it out must be left to time and consideration.

"My object is that in all countries the largest possible number of small shareholders shall enjoy the fullest possible advantages.

"Suppose I was to come to an arrangement with ten large bankers to make the concession over to them, what would happen? They would propose to divide so many millions; they would then distribute to the 'vile multitude,' without spending a penny and with a high premium, five hundred franc shares, taking care to let it be known that, as is very likely to be the case, these shares will one day yield an interest of 20 or 30 per cent.

"Why should we not go direct to the public? The two latest French loans show what can be done with small capital. You will say that the Canal Company will not inspire the confidence which a strongly constituted government enjoys. My answer is that the junction of the Mediterranean and the Indian Ocean, teeming with such immense results, can be so clearly put before the public that the most prejudiced will be convinced that no speculation could offer a better chance of profit to those who take part in it, and when it is found that the cream of the profit has not fallen prey to a few brokers, there will be no lack of shareholders."

It was in order to spread this gospel in England that he spent the spring and summer of 1855 first in London and then travelling throughout the English countryside with his son Charles as his companion. The trip to England was to be a propaganda campaign par excellence. His knowledge of the English language may have been shaky, but his knowledge of the British thinking was uncanny. He knew perfectly well that the British government was itself governed by the British people, and if he could win the consent of the people, the government would necessarily have to give consent, also.

His years in the foreign office had given him friends in all countries and he had no trouble being received in

British society. He met all the right people—he met the queen and her royal consort at a dinner party, and found them among his most interested listeners. Prince Albert even took him away to the royal study for a private conversation on De Lesseps' favorite subject.

But the queen's prime minister was not so easily interested. Through a friend of Lady Palmerston's, De Lesseps was granted an interview in which he asked the prime minister directly what his objections were. Lord Palmerston was seventy years old, full of memories of those years when England and France were bitterest enemies. He could recall the jealousies between the two countries over the influence each sought to have in the Middle East. He was friendly and courteous to De Lesseps but firmly turned a deaf ear to his charm and persuasion.

"I do not hesitate to tell you what my objections are," he said frankly. "They consist in the first place of the fear of seeing the commercial and maritime relations of Great Britain upset by the opening of a new route which, in being open to the navigation of all nations, will deprive us of the advantages we now possess. I will confess to you also that I look with apprehension to the uncertainty of the future as regards France—a future which any statesman is bound to consider from the darkest side, unbounded as is our confidence in the loyalty and sincerity of the emperor; but after he has gone, things may alter."

These were reasons that seemed completely unreal to

De Lesseps. For any country to admit a desire to hold back the progress of all other nations of the world, merely in order to maintain its present supremacy on the seas, seemed selfish enough to lower Great Britain's moral integrity. Said Pasha had taken a completely opposite view from Great Britain's. He had liked De Lesseps' insistence of equal rights for all nations and favors to none —not even Egypt. Yet Said Pasha's Egypt would be gaining in power, of course, while Great Britain would be giving up power she now had.

Even so, the canal's indefatigable promoter was not discouraged. He took his problem straight to the English people. He, a French nobleman, intimate friend of the rulers of several nations, humbled himself to travel from one small English town to another that summer. He was not trying to sell stock. He was not asking for money. He merely asked that all Britons express their opinions publicly, whether they were for or against an oceanic canal in Egypt.

He and his son Charles would go into a strange town, learn the name of its leading citizen, after which they would call on the gentleman and, after explaining his presence in town, Ferdinand would invite the gentleman —usually the mayor—to be chairman of a meeting he was about to hold, to explain to the citizens of the town what was going to be done at Suez. There would be no charge for the lecture.

No one could have worked any harder for converts. Or

with much greater success. At every town he found disciples. After the lecture, De Lesseps would go over his notes, preparing a statement to be given to the local press the next morning. He would order several hundred copies of the paper, which he would take with him to distribute at the next town before the next lecture.

No Englishman running for parliament ever worked as hard for votes. Soon the canal was being talked about in some towns even more than the Crimean War and the Eastern Question.

The jokesters, of course, were still around. *The Daily Mail*, which loyally supported Lord Palmerston, seemed annoyed by what was going on in England that summer.

"The literature of fiction," it editorialized, "is not dead in the land of Alexander Dumas and Ferdinand de Lesseps. The most extravagant romancers are children compared with the great discoverer of a new Pelusium, trying to convince his audiences that 250 sick Europeans and 600 conscripted Arabs will accomplish this stupendous work, without money, without water, without stones . . ."

Before the summer was over, De Lesseps had learned even more about British psychology. The average Englishman was often afraid of his own conclusions. He needed absolute proof that he was right in believing someone else. If De Lesseps hoped to change the British mind to his way of thinking, he must be able to produce irrefutable evidence that the project was not only possible but also practical.

"A lot of folks here in England say the canal can't be built. Even the prime minister says so. And George Stephenson—and he knows engineering. You say it can be. But how do we know you are right?" he was asked again and again.

De Lesseps thought about Galileo. "What makes you think the world moves? Can you prove it?"

Well, he was going to have to prove it. In October he went back to Paris to gather his proofs together.

CHAPTER FOURTEEN

ON OCTOBER 30 De Lesseps called a meeting in Paris. It had been less than a year since his mission in Egypt. But the first rapid progress in his plans had now bogged down in what would have been defeat for most men, but not for one as stubbornly persistent as Ferdinand de Lesseps. Obstacles were merely hurdles to overcome, and he was certain that they would all be overcome eventually.

To his Paris home at no. 9 Rue Richepance, he summoned the men who were to compose The International Commission for the Suez Canal, a committee of international expert engineers. The viceroy insisted that such a committee should make explorations and report their opinions, augmenting the opinions of his own Egyptian engineers. When De Lesseps had first suggested both Linant Bey and Moguel Bey, Said Pasha had demurred.

"Can you ever get two engineers to agree?" he had asked.

"Their agreement would surely strengthen our position," De Lesseps had answered.

Now they were expecting not two but a dozen engineers to agree. They came—Messieurs Renaud and Lieusou representing France, Mr. de Negrelli from Austria,

Mr. Rendel from England, Herr Conrad, Inspector of the Waterstadt and President of the Society of Civil Engineers, from Holland, and the Privy Chancellor Lentze from Prussia. Linant and Moguel Bey came over from Egypt, shivering in the chill Paris weather of late October.

The engineers listened attentively to Linant and Moguel Bey's reports. De Lesseps asked them to give him a statement of their expenses in coming to Paris, for all expenses were to be paid by the newly organized company. But they shook their heads.

"We wanted to come," they said. "We wanted to know what is happening at Suez."

"And you are about to do just that," he told them. "The viceroy has generously set aside a sufficient sum for the company to make a complete survey of the entire project. Could you be ready to leave for Egypt a week from tomorrow?"

They left from Marseilles on the eighth of November. Another birthday for De Lesseps. Would the canal even be started by his next birthday? When one is fifty, one cannot waste time in idle waiting. Or even more idle arguments with Lords Palmerston and Stratford de Redcliffe.

By New Year's the exploration was finished. On the day after New Year's De Lesseps himself, in trailing oriental robes, rode at the head of this party of international engineers as they paraded down the streets of Alexandria on their camels. The viceroy waited for them in the shadow of those two high obelisks called Cleopatra's needles, close by the royal palace. When Ferdinand saw him standing there, he ordered his camel boy to stop. A flick of the boy's stick brought the camel to his knees and De Lesseps stepped warily to the ground.

"What is the news, my friend? What is the news?" called the viceroy.

The count was all smiles. "It can be done," he said. "They are all in agreement. It can be done. And it shall be."

Said laughed softly. "I should have known. Your smiling face should have told me. You look well pleased with life this new year, my good friend."

"Very well pleased," admitted De Lesseps.

That evening the engineers presented their findings. Their formal report would be ready later. But the importance of their agreement made their report already seem final.

"We will develop our reasons for our unanimous conviction in a detailed report, reinforced by hydrographical charts of the bays of Suez and Pelusium, with outlines showing relief of the soil, etc. This is a long and minute report that will occupy several months in preparation. Meanwhile we beg to acquaint Your Highness with our conclusions:

1. The route by Alexandria is inadmissible, both from a technical and an economical point of view.

2. The direct route offers every facility for the execution of the canal itself, with a branch to the Nile, and presents no more than ordinary difficulties for the creation of the two ports.

3. The Port of Suez will open on a safe and large roadstead, accessible in all weathers, with a depth of about thirty feet of water within a mile from shore.

4. The Port of Pelusium, which according to the draft scheme was to be at the extremity of the Gulf, will be established about seventeen miles further west, at a point where there are twenty-five feet of water within a mile and a half of shore, where the anchorage is good and the getting away easy.

5. The cost of the canal and of the works connected with it will not exceed the figure of 8,000,000 pounds, as given in the draft scheme of Your Highness' engineers."

If the viceroy had held any secret doubts of his friend's wisdom, they were completely gone now. He looked at De Lesseps, and found tears in his eyes. Tears of joy. Said Pasha rushed to him and kissed him, a resounding smack first on one cheek and then on the other, holding him by the shoulders. They both began laughing, and everyone present joined them.

The viceroy turned to his guests, the foreign engineers.

"Gentlemen," he said, "you are engineers. You know what it means to watch a great dream begin to become a reality. Now as a reward to you all, for work well done, tonight you shall eat at my table—every one of you— the favorite food of your own country. Our cooks have been busy all day. Their dinner will prove that the canal can serve the whole world. But first, let us all have coffee together."

When at last they gathered in the state dining room, each found his native food: Wild boar from Austria, and pastries from Vienna; mutton and Irish potatoes from Great Britain; cheese from Holland; apricots and dates and melons from Egypt; sausages and candied apples from Prussia; wine and tender green peas and beans and spun sugar candies from France. And the viceroy happily sampled each dish before offering it to his guests. When all were served, Ferdinand looked at his host and grinned.

"What? No macaroni?" he asked.

CHAPTER FIFTEEN

IT WAS amazing how great a change had come over British political thinking in a year's time. It was particularly apparent in what the newspapers called "the Eastern Question." When De Lesseps returned to England in the spring of 1856, he found the way easier than he had hoped. The jokesters had all but abandoned Suez as the target of their sallies. Men of high position and intelligence were asking serious questions about the possibility of cutting across the Isthmus of Suez.

What had first come to the attention of the British newspapers as a crazy scheme of a French crackpot was now beginning to appear not only less crazy but actually possible. Even the great banking houses of Europe were beginning to notice De Lesseps. A committee of international engineers had gone over the canal site with greatest caution, and had been unanimous in their reports of its practicality and even of where and how the cut should be made. The emperor of France had given the project his blessing. But the greatest of all the assets of the company was the contagious enthusiasm and almost fanatical faith of its promoter.

So quickly was public opinion changing in England, so clearly was it now beginning to blow favorably for the canal, that the British government's rejection of the scheme seemed almost a public scandal to those who had become its supporters.

But Lord Palmerston, now eighty years old, had not changed one bit. When a member of parliament rose to ask what the government's opinion was regarding Suez investment, Lord Palmerston answered in words that were both misleading to the member and insulting to the canal's promoter.

"Her Majesty's government certainly cannot undertake to use their influence with the sultan to induce him to give permission for the construction of this canal, because for the past fifteen years Her Majesty's government have used all the influence they possess to keep the scheme from being carried into execution. It is an undertaking which I believe, as regards its commercial character, may be deemed to rank among the many bubble schemes that from time to time have been palmed off on gullible capitalists. If my honorable friend, the member from Bristol, will take my advice, he will have nothing to do with the scheme in question."

De Lesseps was naturally angry. But he could not well challenge the prime minister of Great Britain to a duel. He did the next best thing, however. George Stephenson, the engineer who had disapproved the canal, had built the railroad across Suez and therefore did not desire competition by water. He was then a member of parliament. When Stephenson rose to say that he agreed with everything the prime minister had said, De Lesseps promptly sent him a note. The note inquired whether Mr. Stephenson had meant to imply that the writer was a charlatan seeking to fleece the British public, and requested an answer by return messenger or through a friend who would represent him as his second. Stephenson had no desire to meet the battling Frenchman in any duel. He quickly replied that nothing was further from his mind than implying anything personal against De Lesseps, whose splendid character everyone recognized as the soul of honesty. The Englishman's reply may have disappointed De Lesseps a little, for a duel with Stephenson would have been remarkably good advertising for his canal.

The Crimean War was over at last, and the Eastern Question was solemnly discussed in British journals, in which some supported and some attacked the Suez project. The firman had still not been approved by Turkey, however, but Lord Palmerston's objections had changed somewhat, though they were still as vigorous as ever. Instead of objecting on behalf of his own country's naval supremacy, he now had grown suddenly tender of Turkey's interests and the dangers that might lurk in an interoceanic canal in Egypt.

The Empress Eugénie was still a devoted friend of the project, and she and her royal husband paid a timely social visit to their good friends, Queen Victoria and her German husband. During the visit, the French emperor persuaded the queen to agree to a policy of nonintervention, to allow Turkey herself to decide whether or not to approve the firman. This was construed by the always optimistic De Lesseps as being virtual agreement of the firman, permitting the work to begin at Suez. But when Said Pasha consulted his legal advisors, they did not share De Lesseps' optimism, and insisted that to start without the signed approval of Turkey would open the way to all sorts of political tangles.

Nevertheless, De Lesseps was definitely making progress, even though the actual work could not yet be started. But unless they could start soon, the new stockholders would become anxious and later sales of stock would be far more difficult to make.

The successful building of the canal was actually the meshing of innumerable very different but almost equally vital elements—the financing, the management and planning, the political aspect, and the engineering. But perhaps the most important element, next to faith itself, was the unfailing friendship between a French count and an Egyptian viceroy. Had that friendship been strained a little too far at any stage of the canal's construction, there would be no Suez Canal. The stresses placed upon that friendship were tremendous. So many things could have happened. British threats—going even so far as to threaten that Said be dethroned—could have frightened the viceroy into withdrawing his support, for fear of losing his throne. But he was not so easily bluffed. On the other hand, De Lesseps could, at several stages, have sold out to either France or to England. A country as weak as Egypt, situated on the crossroads of the world's highways, could not hope ever to be completely independent. Yet De Lesseps preserved Egypt's rights with faithful devotion. The two men—ex-teacher and ex-pupil—were bound by a fidelity that was neither occidental nor oriental in character, being as rare a thing and as beautiful, one place as another. Not that there were never differences. There were many of these. But neither man allowed disagreements to affect the very real and very deep affection each felt toward the other. Both were completely possessed by the project, once it was agreed to build, and they were determined that neither whispered threats nor spoken rumors would interfere.

In fact, the very cornerstone of the Suez Canal was this mutual respect and confidence of two men—one young and one beyond middle age. It was to be De Lesseps' eternal regret that Said Pasha did not live to see the canal completed. The viceroy should have been by his side at the grand opening. They had both earned the right to stand before the crowds, watching the two seas mingle. When a man remains so long true to his dream, he should be permitted to watch its fulfillment.

Ferdinand was at the canal site in Suez in the middle of January, 1863, when a messenger came from Alex andria with a message that his friend Said Pasha was desperately ill of a fever and was asking that he be told of his illness. Ferdinand immediately called for his horse to be brought, that he might go as quickly as possible to Alexandria. But he arrived too late. When he entered the palace, they told him that Said Pasha had died and had been buried. He knew only too well that he would never have another friend like him.

He asked Said's saddened wife to give him the key to the tomb that he might look once again at his friend's face. At the tomb, he asked the palace guards who had come with him to remain outside. He wanted to be alone with his friend.

He stood against the rough brick wall, silently weeping. He had not felt such grief since the death of Agathe and his little sons. Once again it seemed to him that God had been uselessly cruel. Said, so many years younger than he was, should have lived a long, long while, and should have seen the final realization of their dream and enjoyed its results for many years. He should have lived that he might have reaped the glory earned by his faithfulness and generosity. It was not fair that he had to die.

"Said," he cried, as he touched the royal sarcophagus, and he felt as though he were making a holy promise, "you once told me you hoped to have your name go down in history as one of Egypt's great rulers. I promise you that it shall be as you once desired."

He went out of the tomb and locked it, tears blurring

his vision. He rode slowly back to the palace, Said's official steward riding beside him. At first Ferdinand could not speak to his companion. After a while, they talked of the viceroy, as each remembered him.

"You remember the cane you gave him?" asked the steward. "He had it with him always, until the very last. He preferred that cane to all others."

De Lesseps smiled. "He had two canes," he suddenly remembered. "We worked out a kind of code with them. When I was with him, and a caller came, if he wanted me to stay on, he would put my cane down beside him. But if he wanted me to leave, he would put down the other cane, and I would make my excuses and go." There were so many happy memories of Said. No one could have had more swiftly changing moods; spoiled child he was at times, clever monarch at others, bosom friend usually, but occasionally ordering his best friend from his presence in anger. Both ruler and agent had been fond of laughter, and they had shared jokes as well as political worries.

"I wonder where that cane is now," said Ferdinand, breaking through his thoughts at last. "I'd like to have it."

When they were back at the palace, he asked the viceroy's wife if he might have the cane. She gave it gladly, knowing in her heart that of all the hundreds and even thousands of people who had known Said, she and Ferdinand de Lesseps would miss him most keenly.

"If only Said could have lived to see the canal finished,"

he kept repeating over and over. "He helped us through all our difficulties. He should have reaped the rewards."

They had gone through so much together—the first stock sales, twenty-five thousand shares in two weeks, at a thousand dollars a share! Neither of them could quite believe it. And the time when all the company officers had come to Alexandria from Paris, to beg the viceroy to let them start digging the canal without the firman, and Said's lawyers would not let them. Finally Ferdinand himself had produced a precedent for the lawyers that made the law on their side, after all. England had asked no permission from Turkey when she had built her railroad across Suez, George Stephenson's railroad. Why, then, should Egypt be asking permission?

At least Said had been by his side that twenty-fifth day of April, 1860, when the engineers and employees and a few loyal supporters, some from foreign countries, had gathered at Pelusium—which he had decided to call Port Said, instead of Pelusium, that his good friend might have the glory that he so richly deserved.

That day, under a marquee where Said had sat with the others, one of the workmen had handed Ferdinand a shovel. As he had looked down at the golden sand of the desert and then up at the red mountains in the distance, he had tried to think of a fitting verse from the Bible with which to dedicate this soil from which had grown the Bible itself. The only fitting verse he could remember was one from Milton.

"Illimitable ocean, without bound,
Without dimension; where length, breadth and height
And time and place are lost."

Then he had dug the shovel deep into the golden sand
and had thrown the sand high in the air and had watched
it come down, touched by the sun now until it was pink
sand, and he had heard Said's voice above all the others,
cheering as though this were a moment to be always held
in the memory. As it would be for both of them.

And because it would have been impossible for Ferdinand to have started any great work without asking God's
blessing upon it, he had said a prayer—a Christian prayer
to a Christian god, for unchristian ears to hear.

"May God bless the building of this great canal, and
see its completion for the good of the world and as an
instrument of peace."

In the very beginning of the work, everything had gone
so well. Said had conscripted workmen, for both he and
De Lesseps had agreed that if men could be conscripted
for war, for killing, how much better it was to conscript
them for work that would mean peace and prosperity to
them. He had often heard them singing as they worked
on all the seven divisions of the long waterway.

Thousands of men, singing together and working for
peace. It had sounded good to him.

And then, preparing his reports for his first stockholders' meeting, proud of the progress he could report,
a message had come from Pelusium from Laroche, the

assistant engineer in charge there. The minister of finance of the Supreme Porte had suddenly appeared at his diggings and had ordered the work stopped immediately. The French consul had refused to protest. Laroche himself had gone on working, saying in fine imitation of his boss, "No one can stop me."

As soon as the news had reached him, De Lesseps had called a meeting of his directors, thankful that he was in Paris at the time. When he had told them what had happened, he had added:

"It is England again, I feel sure. Turkey still sings Britain's song. It means that England has broken her pledge of neutrality and that is an insult to France. However, an agreement that has been broken by one party, is no longer an agreement for the other."

A committee representing the officers of the Suez Canal Company had solemnly called upon the emperor of France that day. In view of the broken agreement, could not His Majesty command that the work be continued? they had asked. And the French consul who had refused to protect French property—could he not be appointed to some other post?

England and Turkey had finally made such a fuss about conscripted labor that Said had stopped the conscription, and after that the work had gone more slowly from lack of sufficient workers. Then as though sent by heaven itself, a whole colony of prisoners, escaped from their prison off the Italian coast, appeared at Suez and De Lesseps had promptly offered to feed and clothe them and give them their wages if they would work on the canal. So he had fed and clothed them and lectured them about the work they were doing, making them feel a deep pride in being a part of history. They had not counted on being completely rehabilitated by their employer, and partly from sheer wonder at their own new-found capacity for goodness, they had made twice as good workmen as most men. De Lesseps still felt proud of the change he had made in them. He had watched over them like a father, for there had been objections in the camp because escaped prisoners were, according to popular opinion, dangerous.

"Men commit crimes only when they are hungry or afraid," De Lesseps had told the fearful ones. "Give them good food and safety and they will become good citizens always." And so it had been.

By February, 1862, the freshwater canal had been ready. By De Lesseps' next birthday in November, the waters of the Mediterranean had filled the canal as far as Lake Timsah, which was where the Jews were said to have crossed the Red Sea when escaping from Egypt under their leader, Moses. This was an historic event that would be long remembered.

A pavilion had been built at Lake Timsah, and all the notables interested in the project were invited to come to see the oceans merge. De Lesseps had himself given the signal for the men to remove that last thin ribbon of earth that divided the two great bodies of water. The earth flew into the air and down again. With a roar, the Mediterranean rushed into Lake Timsah. De Lesseps had lifted his arms and had said in a loud, clear voice:

"In the name of His Highness, Mehemet Said, I now command that the waters of the Mediterranean enter Lake Timsah, by the grace of God!"

What a dramatic and completely satisfying experience that had been! When it was over, Ferdinand had joined the viceroy on the platform.

"It is done!" he had said. "Mon ami, did you see it?"

Said had smiled happily. "I saw. It is done. But there were times when I thought that it never would be."

"I never doubted," Ferdinand had told him then. And it was true. He had always known it would be done. "Did I not tell you again and again and again?"

Said nodded. "You did, mon ami," he answered, with a grin. "So often that I almost stopped believing you."

That had been in November. Now, less than two months later, before the New Year had really started, Mehemet Said was dead from a fever. And his good friend from France felt sadly alone.

CHAPTER SIXTEEN

THE ACTUAL building of the canal took ten years. The first shovelsful of desert sand were dug out of the canal site on April 25, 1859. The grand opening was in November, 1869.

But that ten years passed far more quickly for the canal's promoters than the five years before them, when the whole project at times seemed impossible because of the political embroilments that made the viceroy of Egypt insist on Turkish approval of a firman granting permission to build the canal on Egyptian soil. That approval would have been quickly granted had not Great Britain refused to allow it for reasons entirely selfish. It might produce competition for naval supremacy which was so completely hers at the time. The Ottoman Empire was controlled by an international commission of European countries. The consent of the Supreme Porte meant not only the consent of Turkey, but also of Europe, and only with that consent could the work go ahead without political bickering. There had been that bickering, too. But Fate seemed on the side of De Lesseps, when a sudden uprising in India sent British troops hurrying to the Far East—across the Isthmus of Suez! This broke down the last faint resistance of England. Progress cannot be held back forever. England's shortest route to India was across Suez—whether by land or by water.

Not that those five years of opposition were completely wasted. Much was gained by the time lost. For one thing, they turned an obscure French ex-diplomat into one of the most famous men in the world. For another, they spread the story of Suez throughout the world and made possible the international company of promoters and brought stockholders from most of the countries of Europe. But in spite of all this, there were times when the company treasury was empty, and the future looked black indeed. Only the unfailing optimism and the unflagging energy of Ferdinand de Lesseps, one man alone, the stubborn persistence of one individual holding on to the very end, made the canal possible.

Five years is a long time to a man of sixty. But in those five years of working for the consent of the Supreme Porte, De Lesseps had a chance to clarify his own ideas, hazy in the beginning. He learned much in those years. Not the least of his lessons was one that proved the value of publicity. He took the newspapers into his confidence, and in telling his story, they gained for him the natural human sympathy that is aroused when a courageous and often foolhardy man stands strong and unflinching during attack, refusing to change his course or yield to his attackers, confident of his own rightness.

There were probably times when De Lesseps must have felt as irritated with Said Pasha, his good friend, as with

Lord Stratford de Redcliffe. For Said Pasha, too, was stubborn. In spite of the most eloquent arguments of his good friend from France, he still insisted upon the firman. The country grew weary of the whole business. But Said Pasha knew that unless the entire world wanted such a canal built, his country would soon become a battleground for other nations. This he did not intend to have happen. Not in his lifetime, anyway—not ever, if he could help it.

The five years had shown both De Lesseps and Said that the undertaking was not as simple as they had believed it to be when they started. For instance, the management of the canal would most certainly determine whether Suez would be an instrument of peace or of war. The question had been discussed at that meeting of engineers in Paris, and Prince Metternich of Austria had ideas on the subject that he afterward put into writing. It was agreed that eternal neutrality must be assured the canal in order for it to be of lasting service to world trade. The prince approved De Lesseps' idea that the canal, owned and managed by men of all nations, would be kept neutral for the simple reason that no nation would dare aggression against the combined force of all other nations. But he wanted to make such neutrality certain.

Prince Metternich thought the neutrality clause must be assured by some sort of international power. In other words, the European powers that watched over the Ottoman Empire should grant whatever necessary power would be needed to keep the canal forever neutral. This

day set for the opening. It had been chosen because it was also the empress' feast day, and surely the canal had known no more staunch supporter than Her Majesty, Empress Eugénie.

Once it almost seemed that the opening would have to be postponed. And such a postponement would have been almost impossible at so late a date.

Two days before the opening, one of the assistant engineers came into De Lesseps' office at Suez and sank wearily into a chair. De Lesseps noticed his drawn face and knew there was trouble. By that time, he could recognize trouble quickly. He had seen enough of it.

"What's disturbing you?" he asked.

"Plenty," answered the engineer. "A spike of rock at the south end of Serapeum. It would rip the first vessel that touched it into two pieces."

"Then get rid of it. How long will it take?"

The engineer, already close to exhaustion, shrugged his shoulders. "We'll have to blast first. Then dredge. We can't be done by the sixteenth."

"But we have to be done then. The grand opening can't be postponed. We can't keep the world waiting, while we dredge Serapeum."

The magic of De Lessep's personality in that brief moment brought a smile to the man's face and eased his weariness. No, it was quite true—they couldn't keep the world waiting.

"We'll blast tonight, and get to work in the morning. Perhaps we can be ready, after all," he said.

"Perhaps? I'd like your word, sir, that you will be ready."

And the engineer gave his word—and kept it.

Important visitors began to arrive on the sixteenth. By some miracle the channel at Serapeum had been cleared even sooner than the engineer had hoped. But had the visitors arrived an hour sooner, they would have seen the dredgers at work.

Pelusium had been renamed Port Said, in honor of the viceroy, without whom there would have been no canal. Suez, on the Red Sea, a village with a mere handful of people, completely surrounded by desert, had now blossomed into a thriving town. Ismailia at Lake Timsah, which tradition claimed as the point at which Moses had crossed the Red Sea, was also a town now. And all three canal towns were decked out in their finest oriental splendor. Khedive Ismail spent with a lavish hand, but the results were stupendous. Suez and Ismailia waved hundreds of glowing banners. But Port Said was the gayest of all. Her docks were crowded with yachts and steamers, with large sailing ships and innumerable small craft, with cruisers and warships. And every mast was trimmed for the grand celebration.

It had rained all the while they were blasting and dredging at Serapeum, but on the sixteenth and seventeenth the sun shone its brightest. This pleased De Lesseps, who interpreted it as being but one more sign of heaven's favor. There had been many of these. But then it had seemed to him from the very beginning that Agathe was his partner in the whole project, and all the numerous heavenly favors bestowed upon Suez had been gifts from her. Now their work was ended. He had kept his promise to Agathe. He had built the canal. It was as though the opening of the canal had made it possible at last for him to free himself from this partnership with the dead. Now he could think of himself—and his own future. There was a woman, young and beautiful, who had attracted him.

On the Quai d'Eugénie at Port Said a platform had been built which was to be the speaker's stand. There the great ones would sit. There the speakers would utter historic words. Seldom had so many great ones gathered in one place.

Among the six thousand present were the Empress Eugénie of France, Empress Elizabeth of Austria, the Emperor of Austria, the Crown Prince of Prussia, Prince William of Hesse, the Crown Prince of Holland, and many others equally royal. Charles and Victor de Lesseps, Ferdinand's sons, his brother Theodore, and the French directors of the Suez Canal Company were all present. The Crescent and Star of Islam and the Christian Cross fluttered together in the desert breeze. Had not Egypt been the meeting place of East and West since the beginning of Time? So it would always be. And here at Suez the two civilizations would clasp hands in mutual trade. What better assurance for peace to the world could be found?

Warships of many nations sounded a cannon salute when the French yacht, *L'Aigle*, drew near. On it were the Empress Eugénie and her entourage and the French directors of the canal company.

On the seventeenth, the speeches of dedication occupied the entire morning. The new canal was blessed by a Christian bishop and a Mohammedan priest. The speakers of both East and West had much to say of Mehemet Said, who had bravely granted the concession for this historic moment. They called Ferdinand de Lesseps a second Christopher Columbus, seeking a new route to India and suggested that instead of Isabella of Spain it was Eugénie of France who had been this second discoverer's patron. Trumpets sounded before and after each speech and drums boomed in the distance.

That night the harbors at all three canal towns were lighted by glowing torches. Fireworks poured fountains of colored rain into the water at Port Said, splashing the royal yachts at anchor with their eerie lights. There were balls at Port Said and at Ismailia and at Suez.

At Port Said, on the Quai d'Eugénie was staged the still unfinished opera *Aïda*, composed and directed by the great Signor Verdi for this very special occasion. Though the composer insisted the opera was not yet quite finished, not ready for public performance, here it was being produced for that most special audience, by royal command of the empress of France, and the khedive of Egypt. The khedive had distributed free tickets with a lavish hand to thousands of guests.

Throughout the festivities, Ferdinand de Lesseps, the hero of the entire celebration, was accompanied not only by his two sons and their wives and all his numerous relatives who had believed in him and entrusted their money to the canal, but also by a dark-skinned dark-haired young woman younger than his sons. She was Mademoiselle Louise Hélène Bragard. She was twenty-one years old, the daughter of a Jamaican executive. She was of French, Spanish and Jamaican blood; De Lesseps himself was of French and Spanish ancestry. She was beautiful and charming and was completely adoring toward this ever-young, sixty-four-year-old hero of Suez.

De Lesseps had always been popular with women, but not since Agathe's death had he regarded any one woman with the eyes of romance. He had first been too grieved, and then too poor, and then, in the last decade, too busy for serious love-making. But now he would have time for domestic joys. He might even have children. And never before had he met a woman who made him feel as young and as strong and as joyous as this young girl who danced with him and laughed with him and whose dark eyes adored him. Perhaps, if she would have him, he would marry her.

As they sat watching the unfinished opera of Signor Verdi's a messenger leaned over De Lesseps' chair and whispered:

"My lord, could I speak to you privately? It's—it's the canal, sir. Something has happened at Ismailia."

He offered his apologies to Mademoiselle Bragard and gave her to the care of the empress' party. Then he followed the messenger and heard his story.

"Has the viceroy gone to his quarters?" he asked. He knew it was Ismail Pasha's custom to leave the opera a little before the end, that others might not have to linger because of protocol that demanded no one leave until the viceroy had departed.

It was hours after midnight. Ismail Pasha groaned when De Lesseps was finally admitted to his bed-chamber.

"Not more trouble!" he moaned. "Not this late!"

De Lesseps smiled. "It is never too late for trouble, Your Highness. One of your freighters, Your Highness, neglected to watch the buoys as instructed. As a result, the freighter is grounded and is swung across the canal, completely blocking it. I am going at once to Ismailia. But before I go, I would like your permission, sire—"

He did not need to finish. "If there is no other way to clear the canal—yes. Only then may you blow up the freighter. The canal cannot be blocked tomorrow. Now is that all you want of me? May I go back to sleep?" Ismail Pasha yawned.

"Thank you, sire," murmured Ferdinand. "I envy Your Highness his night's rest. I could use some sleep."

CHAPTER SEVENTEEN

FERDINAND rode to Ismailia as fast as his fine Arabian horse could carry him. The freighter was still there, but to his relief he saw that men were already at work trying to free her. The desert sand was strewn with her cargo. A troop of Egyptian marines was hard at work. De Lesseps watched the work progress and sighed with weary relief when, just at sunrise, the freighter groaned and slid off the sand bar. All that remained now was to reload the cargo. The marines must rejoin their sister ships at Suez, for at eight o'clock they must start through the canal.

"I will go with you," De Lesseps told the commander. "On your ship, I will be able to sleep without interruption."

At eight o'clock on that morning of November 18, 1869, the French royal yacht, *L'Aigle*, led a flotilla of shipping vessels into the canal at Port Said. At precisely the same moment, a fleet of Egyptian warships—on one of which Count de Lesseps was peacefully sleeping—entered the canal at Suez. They were to meet that night at Ismailia.

The Empress Eugénie had missed her favorite cousin. "Where is the Count de Lesseps? Have you seen Cousin

Ferdinand?" she asked, as soon as she left the royal cabin. No one had seen him.

"He was to have been on this ship," she insisted. "What do you think could have happened?"

Mademoiselle Bragard was alarmed. Could something have happened to her hero during the work at the sand bar? Or could he have been thrown from his horse on his way back to Port Said?

At eight o'clock that evening, the French flotilla steamed into Ismailia just as the Egyptian warships arrived from the opposite direction.

At Ismailia that night there was another ball, and Ferdinand de Lesseps, pink-cheeked and bright-eyed, as lively as young Louise Hélène Bragard, put in his appearance. He had enjoyed more than twelve hours of sleep. It was sleep he had badly needed.

The next day the eighty vessels continued their passage through the canal. That night the French ships were at Suez. What changes there had been in the town since the canal had been first started! There had been nothing then but a few wretched huts, for people do not live in places where there is no fresh water to drink. Now the canal had brought them good water and commerce. It had brought life to Suez.

The trip through the canal had excited the Empress Eugénie, a charming woman full of enthusiasms. "I thought I should die of suspense when we were going

through our canal!" she cried. "I was afraid something
might go wrong and we should have had all our hard
work for nothing!"

Her friends laughed, and teased her for talking as
though she had built the canal with her own hands. But
De Lesseps did not laugh.

"Her Majesty can well say 'our canal,' " he told them.
"Her interest has been so generous always that she may
well claim full credit for today's success. And it was a
success, was it not?"

It was a day he had waited to see for so long a time that
now it had come, he could hardly believe it. He needed
the assurance of friends that it had actually happened and
was not merely another part of his old dream.

"It was wonderful! It was beautiful!" sighed the empress.

The count bowed over his sovereign's fingertips as he
pressed his lips to them.

"Your Highness, the speaker was right who said you
were the Queen Isabella of Suez."

Hélène Bragard laughed. "And you, my lord, he said
were Colombo. It is you who discovered Suez—and a new
route to India."

That evening he asked Monsieur Bragard for his
daughter's hand and was accepted. But when he told his
son Charles he intended to marry, Charles shuddered.

"But you cannot be serious! She is so young—so ignorant of the world. You, sir, are my father. I am ten years older than she is. You are my father, and the grandfather of my children. Surely you can't be serious."

"I was never more serious, my son," answered his father.

They were married within a week, the day after the empress of France, at a solemn ceremony on the French royal yacht, had pinned a medal of the French Legion of Honor on Ferdinand de Lesseps' breast, in the name of her husband, Napoleon III, and in the name of France. And Charles, still disapproving, drank a toast to his father's bride.

The next day, as the bride and groom were riding their horses along the bank of the canal, they heard the harsh horn of a freighter.

De Lesseps stopped his horse. "Wait," he said to his bride. "It is our first customer."

They watched until a British ship entered the canal. It was a freighter on its way home from India.

De Lesseps burst out laughing. "Wouldn't you know it!" he cried. "After all the trouble she caused us—it would have to be Great Britain, the first to use our canal."

Many years later, Charles would have been forced to revise his opinion of his father's second marriage. June and December they might be, but they were to live together happily and devotedly for a quarter of a century.

The young wife was to give her husband, as the years passed twelve children, six sons and six daughters. And when the French Panama Canal Company ended in inglorious failure, for which her husband of over eighty would be blamed, her intense and unflagging loyalty and her unclouded faith in him to the day of his death, proved beyond any doubt that the marriage was good.

If he had dreamed of retiring into obscurity at Chesnaye now that the canal was completed, he soon found out that obscurity was no longer possible. He was a great man now. The whole world wanted to honor him.

"Le Grand Français," people were calling him. Crowds would follow him as he walked in the streets or rode his horse through the Bois. Being human, he liked it. But most of his liking was because he could see how such attentions pleased his young wife. Her dark eyes shone with delight at each sign that her husband was one of France's most beloved citizens.

Even England was eager to honor him, now that the canal was actually finished and in use. The British government invited him to visit England the summer following the grand opening. He accepted the invitation in June, 1870. From the day he and his wife arrived in Liverpool until the day they left to return to Paris, their trip was a tour of triumph. In Liverpool the Duke of Sutherland gave a great banquet for them at Stafford House, and the Lord Mayor offered a toast "to the man who has at once brought Madras within twenty days of Liverpool."

The London *Times*, the paper that had fought him so bitterly, now greeted him in its editoral.

"Mr. de Lesseps," said the *Times*, "has arrived in a country which did nothing to help him in the construction of the canal, but which since its opening has had more ships passing through it than all other nations put together. It is this country that will provide him with almost all the dividends which his shareholders will cash. Let that be the compensation which we offer for all the wrongs which we have managed to inflict on him in the past."

In London there was a mammoth reception in his honor at the new Crystal Palace which had just been completed. Thirty thousand people were said to have pushed their way through the crowds, just to get a look at the Grand Frenchman. As many as were close enough to him, and bold enough, shook his hand, and enjoyed his twinkling smile.

The lord chamberlain, in a long and flowery speech, offered him the keys of London, an honor hardly less great than the French Legion of Honor, whose medal he proudly wore on his chest. He responded to the lord chamberlain in the name of Suez, silently hoping, no doubt, that this public ceremony might encourage Great Britain to buy some of that block of 85,000 shares that the viceroy had insisted must be set aside for England and the United States and other more timid nations, who preferred to wait until success was assured before buying stock in it.

Their visit in England was cut short by increasing rumors of war at home. They had barely settled themselves once more at Chesnaye than France reluctantly declared war on Germany, and Napoleon III himself commanded a regiment of his own troops at Sedan. But the name of Napoleon was no longer magic, for the French were defeated at Sedan and the emperor was made a prisoner of war. The Germans laid siege to Paris, and De Lesseps himself helped to guard the Palace of the Tuileries, to protect the Empress Eugénie. He helped plan her final escape, with her fourteen-year-old son, the prince imperial, across the Channel to the affectionate protection of Queen Victoria of England. The empress had scarcely arrived in London before the Tuileries in Paris became a blazing torch against the night sky, a torch set by German hands. By the time the war had ended, France had lost Alsace-Lorraine, her emperor and the empire itself, as for the third and last time, France again became a republic. And this time it was to be forever.

De Lesseps' personal life was happier than it had been in a great many years. At the age when most men were calmly enjoying their grandchildren, he was playing the part of bridegroom and then of a new father. He made a wonderful parent, patient and devoted, understanding, yet lively and active and always amusing. That same charm that made all the world love him also endeared him to his own children. He was their hero and the center of their young lives.

Perhaps his greatest joy was in teaching his new family to ride. Almost before they could walk, he would have them on the back of a horse, sitting in front of him, holding the end of the bridle rein. By the time they were ready for school, most of them were experienced jumpers. Parisians felt the day was off to a good start on those mornings when they came upon The Grand Frenchman riding in the Bois with his small daughters, their long hair flying in the wind, laughing and calling to one another and racing along the bridle paths.

Charles de Lesseps was now his father's agent in the Suez Canal Company. Even after the completion of the canal, there were still tremendous bills to be paid, for its building had been more expensive than the original estimates. The French government had granted a bond issue, but the bonds sold slowly, for money was far from plentiful during the war, and men were not interested in foreign investments. Once or twice things looked so dark that even De Lesseps talked about liquidation of company assets. Then one morning a French banker came to the office of the Suez Canal Company, a man named Laboudy who asked to see Charles de Lesseps.

"I hear your bond issue is not going well," he said to Charles. And Charles could only agree that this was indeed true. "I have come to give you the money," said Laboudy. "How much will it take?"

Charles could not believe his own ears. Monsieur Laboudy's arrival at that particular moment made him almost able to agree with his father's belief that the way God had so often intervened in the building of Suez was proof it was His will that the canal be completed. Here was another proof of that, thought Charles.

"Another seven million francs would see us through," answered Charles, as soon as he could speak again.

"Well, let me buy your bonds, then. I have made money in this war. I would like to spend it for peace."

This ended the financial difficulties of the Suez Canal, and Monsieur Laboudy was to reap the fruits of his generosity and faith many times over. Dividends as high as thirty per cent were finally paid to all Suez investors, and the value of the canal stock rose to astronomical figures. People began to look upon the plump little figure of Ferdinand de Lesseps as a sort of French Santa Claus, and The Grand Frenchman finally heard himself being called also "World Citizen." The title pleased him.

England was indeed using the canal more than any other nation in the world. It shortened the voyage to India by many days, and had increased Great Britain's foreign trade considerably. The company's stock had been doing quite nicely on the Bourse, and England decided that a large block of Suez Canal stock would be a valuable possession. The decision and the opportunity came at the same time. Ismail Pasha, the extravagant khedive of Egypt, who had spent money so recklessly for the dedication party at Port Said, had grown more and more careless of his money, and was now seeking to increase his fortune in order to pay his debts. The only practicable way he knew to do this was by selling his Suez block of stocks and bonds. A French company, which took an option on the Suez stock, let the option go because De Lesseps had already lent Ismail Pasha money, in the name of the company, with the coupons on the bonds as security. This meant that the bonds would yield no income to the buyer for some twenty years.

Suddenly, without any warning that an international deal was being considered, word spread over the world one day that Benjamin Disraeli, Queen Victoria's prime minister, by a brilliant secret move, without calling together his own parliament to act on the sale, had bought Ismail Pasha's Suez holdings, which then amounted to almost one third of the total stock issued. Many Frenchmen bemoaned Disraeli's action, yet grudgingly admired him for his astute statesmanship. De Lesseps, however, was delighted. Now the canal would be safe—and neutral. England's stable hand would be good for its management. France and England would balance each other, and the

THOSE WHO had been brave enough to have faith in the Grand Frenchman and his grand idea soon found themselves amply rewarded. The Suez Canal came into existence at the time steamships were replacing sailing ships, and with steam, foreign trade increased rapidly and in great volume. Speed and shortened distance brought all the countries of the world in touch with one another. They brought, also, both understanding and differences between countries.

England's fear that her supremacy on the seas would be threatened proved to be without reason. England still was the most frequent user of the canal. Her ships went back and forth to India in half the time they had once taken through the Strait of Magellan.

Ferdinand de Lesseps had put almost every cent he had into the Suez Canal. Now he was beginning to realize a profit. As with all men who find themselves in possession of more money than is needed for their family, he looked for other investments equally fortunate. He never found them. But in the search, he helped promote an Eastern Asia railroad and in making an inland sea out of part of the Sahara Desert. Finally when seventy-four years old, he headed a company of French geographers organized for the purpose of building an American canal at Panama that would connect the Atlantic and Pacific oceans. This proved his Waterloo. Distance, climate, and a morass of political intrigue brought about not only the failure of the project but also one of the greatest economic disasters France had ever known. On the day the company office was finally forced to close its doors, after De Lesseps himself had written the telegram that would stop all work on the Panama Canal indefinitely, he suffered a cerebral stroke that made him an invalid until his death.

Charles, the oldest son who had been with him at Suez, had not approved of his undertaking the Panama project. He remembered all too clearly the worries and fears they had gone through at Suez.

"What do you wish to find at Panama?" Charles asked his father. "Money? You will not bother any more about money at Panama than you did at Suez. Is it glory? You have had enough glory. Why not leave that to someone else? And as for us who have worked at your side, are we to have no repose? . . . You succeeded at Suez by a miracle. Be content with accomplishing one miracle in your lifetime, and do not hope for a second."

His hopes for that second miracle did not materialize but when the debacle came, the devotion of his son Charles was better than any miracle of financial success. When the political intrigues were unravelled, both Charles and his father were indicted for bribing government officials.

But Charles took all the blame on his own shoulders, even to serving the sentence that his father might have shared with him, had his health and the affection of the public not saved him. The indictment should not have been made, of course. It was unjust and without sufficient reason. The French government had promised his company a loan and then, without warning, had refused it. There was no more money with which to pay the heavy bills, and a company with no money and no generous Said Pasha to come to the rescue, could not continue.

Yet even in the face of the scandal, the brilliance of the name of Ferdinand de Lesseps remained untarnished as he sat month after month in his wheel chair, staring into space, looking at a magazine upside down. He was still Le Grand Français.

In 1885, when the Panama project had already been started and De Lesseps, at the peak of his greatness, was made a member of the French Academy, M. Renan, in his speech of welcome, said, "People love you and like to see you, and before you have opened your mouth, you are cheered. Your adversaries call this your cleverness; we call it your magic."

Even his own family felt that magic. Louise Hélène, watching him die, was conscious of it. His children, hovering over him, eager to serve him, to bring him medicine, to wheel his chair, knew it, too.

"Man does great deeds by instinct, just as the bird

wings its flight, guided by a mysterious map which it carries within its tiny brain," said M. Renan.

"You have not disguised from yourself the fact that the cutting of the isthmus would serve alternately very varied interests. The great saying, 'I have come to bring not peace but war,' must have frequently occurred to your recollection. The isthmus cuts a strait—that is to say, a battlefield. One Bosporus had sufficed till now to give trouble enough to the world. You have created another, much more important than the first, for it does not place in communication two parts of an inland sea. It serves as a passage of communication between all the great seas of the world. In case of maritime war, it would be the supreme interest, the point for the occupation of which the whole globe would make a rush. You have thus fixed the spot for the great battles of the future."

The first hint of such a battlefield came in 1876 when Egypt staged an anti-foreigner uprising, and England and France, her guardians under an economic alliance, sought to stop it. Several Europeans were killed in the uprising, and England promptly sent her fleet and opened fire on Alexandria. The route to India must not be threatened. France, on the contrary, ordered her troops home. Of course the next step after that, for England, was to move in and set up a military protectorate.

De Lesseps promptly objected, in the name of his company. But England stayed.

M. Renan, at that French Academy dinner at which Ferdinand de Lesseps was introduced to the Academy, summed up the reasons for De Lesseps' election.

"You have caused to blossom once more a flower that seemed faded forever. You have given in this skeptical world of ours, a striking proof of the efficacy of faith and verified in their liberal sense that lofty saying, 'I say unto you that if ye have faith as a grain of mustard seed, ye shall say to this mountain, remove hence, and it shall remove.' The devotion of your staff was immense. . . . All of your men believed that the eyes of the world were fixed upon them and that everyone was interested in their doing their duty.

"It is all this, sir, that in electing you we are anxious to recompense. We are incompetent to appreciate the work of the engineer; the merits of the financier, the administrator, the diplomat are not for us to discuss; but we have been struck by the moral grandeur of the work, by this resurrection of the faith, not the faith in any particular doctrine, but faith in humanity and its brilliant destinies. . . . Your glory consists in having set stirring this latest movement of enthusiasm, this latest manifestation of self-devotion. You have renewed in our time the miracle of ancient days. You possess in the highest degree the secret of all greatness, the art of making yourself beloved."

For almost a century the statue of Ferdinand de Lesseps guarded the canal for which he labored. In 1956, when the Suez Canal once again became the battlefield M. Renan had prophesied, the statue was destroyed. From now on, the canal must serve the world without even a graven image of the genius who created it. But the great purpose for which it was built, to unite the nations of the world through peaceful commerce, must never be forgotten. Suez belongs to the world still. For what other reasons was it ever built?